ACTOR'S GUIDE TO AGENTS

The comprehensive agent guide from Samuel French

Fall 2018

INTRODUCTION 3
ABOUT US. 4

Launch Your Career THREE TIPS TO FINDING AN AGENT 5
SEVEN SECRETS TO FANTASTIC HEADSHOTS 6
RESUME 101 9

Be in the Know AUDITION MONOLOGUES 12
RESOURCES 13

Talent Agent Listings LOS ANGELES 17
NEW YORK 83
CHICAGO 121
REGIONAL 126

INTRODUCTION

You hold the most comprehensive agent guide available. The *Samuel French Actor's Guide to Agents* contains essential industry and contact information for a wide range of talent agencies in Los Angeles, New York, Chicago, and other regional areas of the entertainment industry.

We have outlined for you guild affiliations, performance categories, staff information, details about specialization, and submission requirements that will be vital in your search for representation. Refer to our handy symbol and abbreviation keys detailed below before you begin browsing the listings. Whether you are interested in TV/film, stage, voiceover, commercials, or representation for young people, use this guide to find the best agencies for you!

When you have found your target agents, pick up a set of *Talent Agency Mailing Labels* and full-view window *Actor's Headshot Envelopes* from the Samuel French Actor's Suite. These tools will help you get your foot in the door and get noticed!

Break a leg!
Samuel French

KEY TO SYMBOLS

THEATRE **FILM/TV** **COMMERCIALS**

VOICEOVER **CHILDREN**

LIST OF ACRONYMS

AEA/EQUITY: Actors' Equity Association

AFTRA: American Federation of Television and Radio Artists

AGVA: American Guild of Variety Artists

ATA: Association of Talent Agents

DGA: Directors Guild of America

NACA: National Association of Campus Activities

NATR: National Association of Talent Representatives

SAG: Screen Actors Guild

WGA: Writers Guild of America

ABOUT US

Samuel French was born in Massachusetts shortly after the turn of the 19th century and began publishing *French's American Drama* in the mid-1800s in New York. It quickly became the most extensive and widely distributed catalogue in the United States. French soon acquired a dramatic publishing company in London, originally founded by Thomas Hailes Lacey, and continued to expand his business on both sides of the Atlantic; Samuel French managed the London business while his son, Thomas Henry, took control of the New York operations.

In the late 1800s, Samuel French began publishing contemporary American dramas and helped the amateur theatre movement by making more plays available to "Little Theatres" – a rewarding concept that had never before been done in the industry. By the turn of the century, amateur interest in acting had increased enormously. As the quality and quantity of available plays improved, so the number of amateur groups increased. The seeds of the Little Theatre movement were sown. By the time of WWI, such groups, along with the High School societies, were the firm's best customers. Although both father and son had long since passed away, the NY and London entities continued under the capable hands of their managing partners.

From the mid-1940s to the early '90s, the company witnessed significant growth in its catalogue and business. During this time, the Stock companies, including the League of Regional Theatres, were flourishing; so, too, were the Little Theatres, and Dinner Theatre was proving increasingly popular. From the mid-90s to the present, the Samuel French catalogue has grown substantially with a focus on emerging playwrights, carefully balanced with additional acquisitions of the most prominent American and British playwrights, such as Neil Simon, Tom Stoppard, Edward Albee, August Wilson, David Mamet, and many more!

To this day we strive to cultivate and expand our catalogue to meet the artistic needs of all of our theatres, mindful of how our history has shaped not only our company, but also the theatrical industry as a whole.

FEEDBACK

How can we make it better? We listen to you! Samuel French is committed to providing you with the most accurate information available regarding the acting industry. To ensure that this book meets your evolving needs, we want to hear your comments and suggestions on how we can make this guide better. Send your feedback to: feedback@samuelfrench.com

THREE TIPS TO FINDING AN AGENT

BY DALLAS TRAVERS

One of the most common complaints I hear from actors involves finding the right representation. Snagging a solid agent or manager can be tricky, time-consuming, and expensive. A lot of actors experience the old catch-22: "I need an agent to get work and I need work to land an agent." What's an actor to do?

Whether you feel like you don't have enough time or money to grab the attention of an agent, or you question whether or not you're ready for representation, you can begin planting seeds with prospective agents easily and inexpensively. All you need to do is commit to these small steps.

APPLY A LASER BEAM FOCUS

I'm a big believer in "doing less more often," so narrow your agent list to a manageable target group of about ten agencies. Ask for recommendations from fellow actors and any industry connections, such as casting directors, producers, acting coaches, etc. Do you have a peer with representation whose career you admire? Research their agency. The Hollywood Creative Directory, available as a reference book in many libraries, and IMDB Pro are good resources to help locate names and contact information for anyone in the industry. Don't forget to plug-in to online forums such as the Hollywood Happy Hour Yahoo Group. You will be amazed by how easily you can access up-to-date information about any agent you may be researching.

REACH OUT ON THE CHEAP

People often think good marketing costs money, but there are numerous effective ways to get in touch with agents without breaking the bank. You might market to your target agents by e-mailing, calling the office, sending a fax, dropping off a headshot, or asking a friend to make a referral call on your behalf. Not only are each of these steps free or inexpensive, but they're also highly effective.

Remember, you don't have to knock an agent's socks off with your fancy marketing package. You're better off applying the Rule of Seven and sending out small, inexpensive touches on a regular basis.

MAKE IT PERSONAL

I'd say the most effective way to secure good representation (other than booking great work) is to rely on referrals. Think about who you know that might be willing to recommend you to their agent. Do you have a teacher or friend who could provide a solid recommendation? If so, ask them to lend a hand in your agent search process.

If you can't get any referrals, then be your own best referrer. Show up to your prospective agent's office and drop off your materials. Ask for a meeting and share why any agent would benefit from working with you.

SEVEN SECRETS TO FANTASTIC HEADSHOTS

BY DALLAS TRAVERS

Your headshot is the ship of all ships. It's your calling card. This 8×10 piece of paper speaks volumes for you before you ever enter a room. But not all headshots are created equally folks, and while you are on your journey toward stardom, your headshot has a heavy load to bear.

Most actors utilize a commercial headshot along with a theatrical headshot. Here's the problem though: these photos usually feature a smiley-faced actor and a frowny-faced actor; neither speak to that actor's unique castability. Until your resume stands alone, your headshot must clearly and specifically explain how you're best cast. So, a handsome photo alone won't cut it. Casting directors are busy people and in order to stand out, you must convey a clear, specific message. Make their job easy. They're looking for the right actors for their projects and it's your job to showcase how right you are. Your photos must be specific.

In an effort to be specific, many other actors own multiple photos featuring them in all kinds of get-ups, like a lab coat, an argyle sweater and glasses, or even a police officer's uniform. While these headshots are very specific, they don't showcase your character, they only highlight a caricature. You must, must, must avoid this at all costs. Yeah, your shots must be specific, but they must also be authentic and believable. Casting directors may be busy, but they're not stupid. They don't need to see you wearing scrubs in order to call you in for an audition as a nurse. Don't rely on costumes or gimmicks to convey your specific castability.

You don't need a ton of specific photos with lots of specific costumes. You only need one to three key photos that speak to your castability in a drama, a comedy, and as a specific character such as a villain, a blue-collar guy, a welfare mom, or a sexy bombshell. It is possible to have headshots that are both specific and authentic. Let me show you how.

SHOWCASE THE REAL YOU

No matter what the role, you're the one being hired for the job. Who you are as a human being affects each role you book, so you've got to know yourself, know how others perceive you, and be willing to showcase your specific and authentic self. Yup, that's right – you get to be you, and the more you showcase your glorious self, the more easily success will meet you. Be your best self. Know who you are and embrace it. Do that, and you'll easily capture a riveting dramatic photo, a charming comedic photo, and perhaps an honest character shot or two.

CREATE A TAGLINE

Now that you've outlined the types of roles you are likely to book, it's time to develop the character. Create some phrases this character would say and think the thoughts of that character during your shoot. Doing so will keep you focused on the core message of your castability so you can convey that energy through your eyes and your expression.

If you play commanding characters, you might think something like, "I'm in charge, here." If you play quirky and fun-loving comedic types, your tagline could be, "You're never going to believe this!" or "This is fun!" If you play dark, brooding roles, your tagline might be, "I've got a secret," or "Trust me...really."

Just develop the character enough to pinpoint possible taglines so you can convey the energy of your niche without the need for costumes, props, or gestures.

COMMUNICATE CLEARLY

Most actors show up to a photo shoot with just a pile of clothes and a dream. Communication with your photographer is imperative. If you can articulate the types of roles you want to book in a way they can understand, the pressure is off. Now you can do your thing feeling confident that your photographer will work his or her magic. Illustrate your character by drawing parallels to other people. If you book sexy roles, are you Angelina Jolie-sexy or Sarah Jessica Parker-sexy? Both women are sexy, but very different. Communicate clearly enough so you know you're on the same page as your photographer. You'll be glad you did.

LESS IS MORE

Don't get too hung up on wardrobe. The perfect wardrobe is one that you don't notice. That said; make purposeful, thoughtful choices about what you wear in your shoot. Subtle hints can help illustrate who you are without slapping someone in the face with a gimmick. Dress from the ground up. The shoes you wear, whether you are sitting or standing, affect the energy in your face during the shoot.

Once you know the message you're going for, ask yourself, "How can I convey this message in the most subtle way?"

MAKE THE CONNECTION

Have you ever had a conversation with someone who couldn't quite make eye contact with you? While you attempt to connect with this person, they stare at your forehead, your chest, or the top of your head. Though you continue to speak, you quickly begin to feel self-conscious or distracted by the lack of eye contact.

When choosing your headshot, make sure you can make direct eye contact with the person on the page. Print the photo out and hold it out two-to-three feet in front of you. As you look at the photo, can you lock eyes with the person on the page? Eye contact is essential to creating the connection you desire with casting directors, agents, and anyone else who happens to eye your headshot.

LET GO A LITTLE

Prepare for your shoot, but then let it all go so you can actually enjoy the experience and allow your true self to shine through. You're gonna have lots and lots of headshots throughout your career. Some will work better than others, but none of them will really make or break you. You must relieve yourself (and your photographer) of the pressure around needing the perfect photo. Forget about the money you've spent. Forget about your nerves, your needs, and your time. Just enjoy the shoot. Part of an actor's job is getting your photo taken, which if you ask me is a pretty cool gig.

AND ANOTHER THING...

Remember that the sole purpose of your headshots is to get you hired. The way to do that is with riveting photos that showcase the real you and speak clearly to your castability. It doesn't matter if you're smiling or not. It doesn't matter if your head is off-center, or the photo is cropped tight to your head. It doesn't matter if the photo is horizontal or vertical. It doesn't matter if it's a close-up or shows a little body. What matters is that the photos capture people's eyes and showcase the real you.

THESE ARTICLES WERE ORIGINALLY FEATURED ON WWW.DALLASTRAVERS.COM

Dallas Travers is the leading expert on business strategy for actors. She teaches actors the career and life skills often left out of traditional training programs. Her groundbreaking book, *The Tao of Show Business*, garnered five awards, including first prizes at The Hollywood Book Festival, the London Festival, and the National Indie Excellence Award. Through her workshops, Dallas helps thousands of actors increase their auditions, produce their own projects, secure representation, and book roles in film, television, and on Broadway. She is a certified life coach and entrepreneur with over a decade of experience implementing marketing and mindset strategies that work.

In 2012, Dallas was accepted into a Masters program for Spiritual Psychology. That fall, she won the Bronze Stevie Award for Women in Business, "Maverick of the Year," an honor given to women who create positive change in their industry. Her book, *The Tao of Show Business*, is now part of the college curriculum at Virginia Commonwealth University, CalArts, and UCLA Extension. She is also guest faculty for the MFA program at CalArts and a monthly columnist for Backstage, the leading information source for her industry. Dallas was named a 2013 Business Excellence Award Finalist for Young Entrepreneurs and, most recently, her company was named a Blue Ribbon Dream Big Small Business of the Year by the Chamber of Commerce.

RESUME 101

BY DALLAS TRAVERS

The time-honored expression "First impressions are everything" is a mantra to live by when preparing your resume. You should apply considerable thought and attention to detail in your preparation, as it is your calling card to opportunity. A great resume will not guarantee you an audition; however, a bad one will surely be dismissed. We have prepared a list of what to do and what not to do when writing a resume to help guide you through the process:

DO

- Check for spelling and grammatical errors
- Make it easy to read
- Limit it to one page
- Update your resume when you have a new project
- Attach your resume to the BACK of your headshot
- Include any union affiliations
- Have someone else proof read
- Use a font that is easy to read and no less than 12 point
- Organize your experience in sections i.e. Theatre, Film and Television, etc.
- Include your real height and weight
- If over age twenty, drop high school credits
- If over age thirty, time to drop college credits
- Always include a "Special Skills" section, and be honest – special or unique skills can open doors for you
- "Less is more," so keep it current

DON'T

- Add your personal address or Social Security number
- List special skills that you cannot do on the spot
- Provide reviews or newspaper clippings pertaining to previous performances
- Include non-union status
- State your age; use an age range instead
- List roles that are outside your age range
- Let your resume hang over the side of your headshot: trim the margins
- Lie

SAMANTHA FRENCH

AEA   High Soprano w/belt (E3 to D6)   Blonde hair/Hazel eyes   5'4", 130 lb   Age: 22-30

samantha@samuelfrench.com   917-867-5309

THEATRE

Much Ado About Nothing	Hero	Classic Stage Company, Tony Speciale, Dir.	NYC
Our Town	Emily	Royal Academy Dramatic Art , John Adams, Dir.	London
Mack and Mabel	Mabel	Mondavi Center, Mindy Cooper, Dir.	California
The Whale	Ellie	Center REP Conservatory, Michael Butler, Dir.	California
She Kills Monsters	Tilly	Gene Frankel Theatre, Tyne Rafaeli, Dir.	NYC
Rocky Horror Show	Janette	UC Davis Mainstage, Mindy Cooper, Dir.	California
See Rock City	Kate	Mondavi Studio Theatre, Patricia Miller, Dir.	California

FILM CREDITS

Perks of Being a Wallflower	Featured Role	Noetic Productions, Garette Henson, Dir.

TRAINING

MFA Acting: Columbia University 2013
RADA Shakespeare Training, London
BA Dramatic Art: UC Davis 2010
ACT Summer Training, San Francisco

Shakespeare/Voice: Kristin Linklater, Andrea Haring
Acting: Andrei Serban, Anne Bogart
Movement: Niky Wolcz, Daniel Irizarry
Singing: Kate Johnson, NYC

SPECIAL SKILLS

Wide singing range, conversational French, basic ballet / jazz / tap, violin / fiddle, stage combat experience, Southern and British accents, singing specialties: classical / musical / folk / jazz.

SAM FRENCH

Age Range: 22-30

SAG

Height: 6'3"
Weight: 230 lbs
Hair: Brown
Eyes: Brown

Cell: (310) 867-5309
Email: sam@samuelfrench.com

FILM

Offline	Lead - Kurt	Warner Bros.	Peter Monsaert, Dir.
J. Edgar	Featured - Bar Owner	20th Century Fox	Clint Eastwood, Dir.
Burn After Reading	Featured - Mail Man	Coen Brothers	Ethan Coen, Dir.

TELEVISION

The Wire, Season 4	Featured - Police Officer	HBO/The Wire Productions

STAGE

Macbeth	Banquo	Classic Stage Company
The Cherry Orchard	Yermolay Lopakhin	Flamboyan Theater
Orphans	Treat	Red Brick Theater
The North Plan	Bob Lee	The Secret Theatre
very still & hard to see	James	Manhattan Theater Society

COMMERCIALS

Conflicts Available Upon Request

TRAINING

Eastern Michigan University	MFA Acting
NYU - CAP 21	Music Theatre Intensive Program

SPECIAL SKILLS

Dialects: Irish, English, Scottish, Southern, Australian.
Experience: Jousting, Horseback Riding, Broadsword, Rapier, Dagger, Drive Standard or
Automatic, Singing

AUDITION MONOLOGUES

Looking for audition material? Check out these Samuel French titles with monologues for auditions, and break a leg!

MONOLOGUES FOR WOMEN: DRAMA

Smudge by Rachel Axler

Informed Consent by Deborah Zoe Laufer

Havana Journal by Eduardo Machado

The Mnemonist of Dutchess County
by Josh Koenigsberg

Quality of Life by Jane Anderson

Prayer for My Enemy by Craig Lucas

brownsville song by Kimber Lee

You Got Older by Clare Barron

Keely and Du by Jane Martin

FUBAR by Karl Gajdusek

A Great Wilderness by Samuel D. Hunter

MONOLOGUES FOR WOMEN: COMEDY

Precious Little by Madeleine George

House of Blue Leaves by John Guare

Shirley Valentine by Willy Russell

Dead Man's Cell Phone by Sarah Ruhl

Bad Jews by Joshua Harmon

Seminar by Theresa Rebeck

Single Black Female by Lisa B. Thompson

The Submission by Jeff Talbott

It Had To Be You
by Renee Taylor and Joseph Bologna

Cheaters by Michael Jacobs

MONOLOGUES FOR MEN: DRAMA

Fences by August Wilson

The Dresser by Ronald Harwood

My Mañana Comes by Elizabeth Irwin

Havana Is Waiting by Eduardo Machado

Quality of Life by Jane Anderson

Prayer for My Enemy by Craig Lucas

A Steady Rain by Keith Huff

Back Back Back by Itamar Moses

4,000 Miles by Amy Herzog

brownsville song by Kimber Lee

The Mnemonist of Dutchess County
by Josh Koenigsberg

MONOLOGUES FOR MEN: COMEDY

Late, A Cowboy Song by Sarah Ruhl

Trip Back Down by John Bishop

Time of Your Life by William Saroyan

Division Street by Steve Tesich

The Irish Curse by Martin Casella

Bad Jews by Joshua Harmon

Frisky & the Panda Man by Ross Howard

Seminar by Theresa Rebeck

Mirror, Mirror by Sarah Treem

The Submission by Jeff Talbott

The Flick by Annie Baker

RESOURCES

ACTORS ACCESS
WWW.ACTORSACCESS.COM

Operated by Breakdowns Services, who assist top level producers and casting directors in the casting process. The site delivers casting calls for actors. It's a great site to start your acting career.

Actors Access website states: "Registration is free! There is no charge to register and establish your account on Actors Access. By doing so, you put your Profile into the Breakdown Services database which is searched by Casting Directors when they are searching the database looking for specific talent. You can optionally receive email notification of the latest roles posted that meet certain criteria in your Profile. You can email out a link that links back to your material that you wish the recipient to see.

As a registered Actors Access user, you can post two photos for free and additional photos for only $10 each. And you can freely swap out either or both of your two free photos as often as you wish with new photos. Create and maintain your online resume that is accessible to casting whenever you make a submission. This resume is also linked to via your agent or manager if you are represented, thus updating your resume for 'everyone' at one time is fast and easy. Create your online Profile that is searched by casting and also provide certain criteria for optionally receiving email notification of the latest Breakdowns and roles posted that fit the selected criteria.

You will be able to read all of the available Breakdowns posted throughout the day on Actors Access. Simply log in with your username/password established when you register for free and check out the Breakdowns whenever you wish 24/7.

When reviewing the Breakdowns that casting has posted for actors on Actors Access (these are different than casting notices posted for agents), as a registered Actors Access user you have the ability to make direct electronic submissions to casting for roles listed that fit your Profile and casting's requirements. As a subscriber to our Showfax service, you can make unlimited electronic submissions on Actors Access at no charge. It comes with your Showfax subscription. As a non-Showfax subscriber, you can also make electronic submissions on Actors Access and there is a $2.00 processing charge. For more information about subscribing to Showfax and its additional benefits, Showfax site atwww.showfax.com and click the "Subscribe" link that you will see at the top of the pages. Currently a one year subscription to Showfax is being offered for only $68 per year – which entitles you to unlimited electronic submissions on Actors Access at no additional cost."

ACTOR'S EQUITY
WWW.ACTORSEQUITY.ORG

The labor union that represents Actors and Stage Managers. Equity seeks to advance, promote and foster the art of live theatre as an essential component of our society. Equity negotiates wages and working conditions and provides a wide range of benefits, including health and pension plans, for its members.

AUDITION UPDATE
WWW.AUDITIONUPDATE.COM

Audition Update and Callback Corner are useful resources for actors auditioning for equity calls in New York City. This online forum allows actors to post information in real-time regarding the current status of auditions taking place at the moment, allowing the actor to be better informed about the scope of their opportunities for the day.

BACKSTAGE
WWW.BACKSTAGE.COM

Backstage magazine was created in December 1960 and has now expanded to an online resources for actors across the country. Backstage features articles about the acting industry and lists casting notices for theatre, film, TV and video, commercials, modeling, voiceover, and other entertainment related events and jobs. To view complete notices and to submit yourself for casting calls, Backstage requires an online subscription, but non-subscribers are still able to search the listings. Besides performance hubs New York City and Los Angeles, they publish notices for dozens of other cities across the United States and Canada, including Chicago, San Francisco, Boston, Miami, Philadelphia, Denver, Seattle, Vancouver, and many more.

SAG/AFTRA
SCREEN ACTORS GUILD/
AMERICAN FEDERATION OF TELEVISION AND RADIO ARTISTS
WWW.SAGAFTRA.ORG

SAG and AFTRA are now one union. The union represents actors, announcers, broadcasters journalists, dancers, DJs, news writers, news editors, program hosts, puppeteers, recording artists, singers, stunt performers, voiceover artists and other media professionals. Members are the faces and voices that entertain and inform America and the world.

Directory Listings
TALENT AGENTS

Los Angeles
New York
Chicago
Regional

ABOVE THE LINE AGENCY

468 North Camden Drive, #200, Beverly Hills, CA 90210
Telephone: 310-859-6115 **Fax:** 310-859-6119
Website: www.abovethelineagency.com
Departments and Staff:
    President - Rima Bauer Greer;
    VP - Bruce Bartlett; Assistant - Leslie Lewis
Ages Represented: 18+
Details: This agency represents actors, writers, and directors for film, TV, books, and other media.
Tips: Submit materials and apply through website.
[DGA, WGA]

ABRAMS ARTISTS AGENCY

750 North San Vincente Boulevard, East Tower, 11th Floor, Los Angeles, CA, 90069
Telephone: 310-859-0625 **Website:** www.abramsartists.com
E-Mail: contactLA@abramsartists.com
Departments and Staff:
    Chairman, CEO - Harry Abrams;
    Senior VP - Alec Shankman; VP - Marni Rosenzweig;
    Commercials, Youth Division - Jeremy Apody;
    Stage Entertainment - Todd Cameron;
    Youth Division, Motion Pictures, TV - Pamela Fisher
Details: This is a top ten agency. They represent a wide variety of talent, including actors, dancers, musicians, writers, sports figures, composers, speakers and lecturers, comedians, music artists, and producers. They provide services to both Los Angeles and New York City.
Tips: Headshots and resumes are accepted by mail only. Interviews are granted by appointment only. Representatives also attend showcases.
[DGA, WGA, ATA, NATR, SAG/AFTRA, AEA]

AC TALENT AGENCY LLC

8447 Wilshire Boulevard, PH, Beverly Hills, CA 90211
Telephone: 323-878-0800 **Website:** www.actalentagency.com
E-Mail: info@actalentagency.com
Departments and Staff:
    Owner/Agent - Anna Chudoba Womack
Ages Represented: 18+
Details: Their specialty is models for trade shows, print, hosting, live events, and catalogs. They also seek work for actors in TV shows, films, and numerous commercials.

NOTES

Tips: Submit materials by mail or email. Also feel welcome to send postcards and invitations. Interviews are by appointment only.
[SAG/AFTRA]

ACROSS THE BOARD TALENT

14542 Ventura Boulevard, Suite 201, Sherman Oaks, CA 91403
Telephone: 323-761-0282   **Fax:** 323-825-2281
Website: www.atbtalent.com
E-Mail: info@atbtalent.com
Departments and Staff:
    President - Guy Kochlani;
    VP - Todd M. Eskin; Agents - Hallie Douglas
Details: This agency delivers a tailored client experience by staffing seasoned agents, while building a client roster of higher profile talent. ATB Talent has specialized departments including film/TV, theatre, and commercials.
Tips: Only hardcopy submissions accepted to be sent to the Woodland Hills, CA address for consideration in both New York and Los Angeles offices. Mark new submission envelopes "New Faces".
[SAG/AFTRA, AEA, NON-UNION]

ACT ONE TALENT AGENCY

23890 Copper Hill Road, #236, Los Angeles, CA 91354
Telephone: 323-306-6002   **Website:** www.actonetalent.com
E-Mail: Info@ActOneTalent.com
Details: Represents actors for theatrical, as well as commercial and print for a variety of big name companies, such as McDonalds, Panasonic, and Budweiser.
Tips: Please email resumes in PDF format with photos as JPG attachment. They no longer accept hard copy submissions or cold phone calls. In their application actors must link to a sample video of their work on Actors Access, YouTube, etc.

ACTORS LA AGENCY

12435 Oxnard Street, North Hollywood, CA 91606
Telephone: 818-755-0026   **Fax:** 323-395-0455
E-Mail: actorsla@gmail.com
Departments and Staff:
    Owner - Sharon Morris
Details: This agency represents actors for film, TV, and commercials. They will also work with voiceover artists, stunt artists, comedians, models, hosts & MCs, and magicians.

Tips: This agency accepts submissions by email only. Interviews are by appointment only
[SAG/AFTRA]

AFFINITY ARTISTS AGENCY

5455 Wilshire Boulevard, #1010, Los Angeles, CA 90036
Telephone: 325-525-1221   **Website:** www.affinityartists.com
E-Mail: info@affinityartists.com
Departments and Staff:
Agency Director/Talent Agent - Ross Grossman;
Film/TV - Erich Smith; Film/TV - Wendy Wheaton
Ages Represented: 5-75
Details: This agency represents talent in all areas: theatre, film, TV, and commercial. They will also work with models and comedians. They have offices in New York.
Tips: Submit materials by mail or email. Interviews are made by appointment only.
[AFM, AEA, WGA, DGA, SAG-AFTRA]

AGENCY FOR THE PERFORMING ARTS

405 S Beverly Drive, Beverly Hills, CA 90212
Telephone: 310-888-4200   **Fax:** 310-888-4242
Website: www.apa-agency.com
Departments and Staff:
President/CEO - Jim Gosnell; Sr. VP, Talent - Jeff Witjas;
Sr. VP/Head, Talent Dept. - Ryan Martin;
VP, Talent - Paul Santana; VP, Talent - Rob Kim
Ages Represented: 12+
Details: This is a top ten agency. With offices in New York and Nashville, Agency for the Performing Arts represents actors for film, TV, and theatre. They also represent composers, writers, comedians, music artists, hosts & MCs, producers (film and music), directors, and variety artists.
Tips: This agency accepts materials via industry referral only. However, they will accept postcards and invitations.
[AFM, DGA, WGA, ATA, SAG/AFTRA, AEA]

AKA TALENT AGENCY

6310 San Vicente Boulevard, #200, Los Angeles, CA 90048
Telephone: 323-965-5600   **Fax:** 323-965-5601
Website: www.akatalent.com   **E-Mail:** aka@akatalent.com
Departments and Staff:
Owner/Agent, Commercial - Doug Ely; Owner/Agent, Commercial - Mike Abrams;

NOTES

Owner/Agent, Commercial - Pamela Porter;
Head Agent, Theatrical - Gregg A. Klein;
Director, Business & Affairs - Jeremy Jones;
Agent, Theatrical - Chip Hooley; Agent, Hosting - Kerri
Boyd; Agent, Personal Appearances - Michael Brooks;
Associate Agent, Theatrical - David Stieve;
Associate Agent, Youth - Lo Brown

Ages Represented: All ages.

Details: This agency books work for theatre, film, TV, commercials, and voiceover. They work with actors, broadcast journalists & newscasters, and hosts & MCs.

Tips: This agency accepts materials via industry referral only; unsolicited materials are not reviewed. Additionally, interviews are by appointment only.

[ATA, SAG/AFTRA, AEA]

ALLENSWORTH ENTERTAINMENT, INC.

433 North Camden Drive, Fourth Floor, Beverly Hills, CA 90210
Telephone: 323-333-5493 **Fax:** 952-402-1226
Website: www.allensworthentertainment.com
E-Mail: info@allensworthentertainment.com
Departments and Staff:
Owner/Theatrical/TV - Stephanie Allensworth;
Commercial - Sandy Kaye

Details: This agency works with both actors and models. They will book work in film, theatre, TV, and commercials. They have a Minneapolis branch.

Tips: This agency accepts materials through email: literary@ allensworthentertainment.com. They have interviews by appointment only.

[SAG/AFTRA]

ALMOND TALENT

8217 Beverly Boulevard, Suite 8, West Hollywood, CA 90048
Telephone: 323-934-5500 **Website:** www.almondtalent.com
E-Mail: info@almondtalent.com
Departments and Staff: Owner/Talent Agent - Aur-Aelion Israel
[SAG/AFTRA, AEA]

ALVARADO REY AGENCY

7906 Santa Monica Boulevard, #205, West Hollywood, CA 90046
Telephone: 323-656-2277 **Fax:** 323-656-2299

Website: www.alvaradorey.com
E-Mail: sendabcd@gmail.com
Departments and Staff:
Owner/Agent - Nikkolas Rey;
Agent - Cynthia Becks; Sub-Agent/Commercial - Alex Lara;
Ages Represented: 2-64
Details: This agency specializes in theatre, film, TV commercials, and print. They usually represent Hispanic and European Actors, people for soap operas, and voiceover, and actors with a background in improvisation.
Tips: They accept email submissions. If you submit via email, do not attach files, instead send content in the body of the email. Alvarado Rey accepts postcards and invitations. Interviews here are by appointment only.
[SAG/AFTRA, AEA, ATA]

AMATRUDA BENSON & ASSOCIATES, INC.

433 North Camden Drive, 4th Floor, Beverly Hills, CA 90210
Telephone: 310-276-1851 **Fax:** 310-276-3517
Website: www.abatalent.com **E-Mail:** info@abatalent.com
Departments and Staff:
Owner/Print/Commercial   -   Kimberly   Gola;
Adult Commercial - Tim Le; Film/TV - Joseph Le
Ages Represented: 5+
Details: ABA represents actors and models for film, TV, commercials, and commercial print. They are especially interested in youth from 5-15, teens, and young adults.**Tips:** This agency accepts submissions through mail or email. Interviews and meetings are by appointment only. Postcards and invitations are accepted.
[SAG/AFTRA]

ANGEL CITY TALENT

4741 Lairel Canyon Boulevard, Valley Village, CA 91607
Telephone: 323-656-5489 **Fax:** 323-656-5408
Website: www.angelcitytalent.biz
E-Mail: angelcitysubmissions@gmail.com
Departments and Staff:
Owner/Agent - Mimi Mayer
Ages Represented: All ages.
Details: Angel City Talent has solidified itself as a fierce competitor within the entertainment industry. Angel City focuses on maintaining a solid, reliable and innovative roster of film, theatre, TV, commercial, print, and hosting talent.

Tips: They only accept submissions through email. Refer to the website for explicit instructions for submission. No attachments accepted. No drop-offs or walk-ins, no exceptions. They request that those seeking represenation refrain from calling the office. **[SAG/AFTRA, ATA, AEA, WGAW]**

ANN WAUGH

4741 Laurel Canyon Boulevard, Suite 210,
Valley Village, CA 91607
Telephone: 818-980-0141 **Fax:** 818-980-4835
Departments and Staff:
  Owner/Theatrical - John Hugh; Commercials/Theatrical - Connie Hamilton;
  Assistant - Caitlin Eubanks
Ages Represented: All ages.
Details: Ann Waugh Talent represents talent for theatre, TV, film, commercials, and print modeling. They work with many character types.
Tips: Submissions should be sent via mail only, and theatrical submissions are by referral only. Interviews only by appointment. They are currently seeking character types, and actors of Asian descent.
[SAG/AFTRA, AEA]

APRIL MILLS

P.O. Box 1983, Burbank, CA 91507,
Telephone: 818-667-9529 **Fax:** 866-667-9529
Website: www.aprilmillsentertainment.com
E-Mail: submissions.aprilmills@gmail.com
Ages Represented: 0-25
Details: This talent agency specializes in kids, young adults, and twins of all ages.
Tips: Submissions (pictures and resume) can be sent via email.

AQUA TALENT

9000 Sunset Boulevard, Suite 700, Los Angeles, CA 90069
Telephone: 310-859-8889 **Fax:** (310) 859-8898
Website: www.aquatalent.com **E-Mail:** aqua@aquatalent.com
Departments and Staff:
  Owner/Head of Commercial - Lawrence Har;
  Theatrical - Courtney Peldon; Print/Non-Union - Alex Leedy
Details: Founded in 2004, this agency represents all types of actors for TV, film, commercials, and theatre.

Tips: Submissions are accepted by mail and through the website. Interviews are by appointment only. They are open to submissions from talent of any kind.
[SAG/AFTRA, NON-UNION, ATA, AGVA, AEA]

ARLENE THORNTON AND ASSOC.

12711 Ventura Boulevard, #490, Studio City, CA 91604
Telephone: 818-760-6688 **Fax:** 818-760-1165
Website: www.arlenethornton.com
E-Mail: oncamera@arlenethornton.com
Departments and Staff:
    President/Voiceover Agent - Arlene Thornton;
    Booth Director - John Lohr, Larry Riess;
    On-Camera Agent - Janet Tscha;
    Voiceover Assistant - Myrna Valenzuela;
    On-Camera Assistant - Jeffrey Rizzi
Details: This agency specializes in the representation of voiceover artists and commercial actors. They look for actors of all types including children, foreign language speakers, and British talent.
Tips: This agency accepts submissions via email to voiceover@ arlenethornton.com or oncamera@arlenethornton.com. Interviews are by appointment only.
[SAG/AFTRA]

ARTISTIC TALENT

5437 Laurel Canyon Boulevard, #111, Valley Village, CA 91607
Website: www.artistictalentla.com
E-Mail: artistictalentinc@gmail.com
Departments and Staff:
    Theatrical Representative - Annette Robinson;
    Commercial Representative - Marci Polzin
Ages Represented: All ages.
Details: This agency represents for commercial and theatrical.
Tips: For representation send inquiries via email to artistictalentInc@gmail.com. In the subject line state "Seeking Representation." No phone calls are accepted.

ATLAS TALENT AGENCY

8721 Sunset Boulevard, West Hollywood, CA 90069
Telephone: 310-324-9800 **Website:** www.atlastalent.com
E-Mail: info@atlastalent.com
Departments and Staff:
    Promos/Trailers/Documentaries/Animation - Heather Vergo;

Priscila Torre;
Commercial Voiceover - Carli Silver;
Business Affairs - Ian Lesser
Ages Represented: 18+
Details: This agency primarily works in voiceover for promos and commercials. They have an office in New York.
Tips: Email and mail submissions are accepted, but this agency prefers email to info@atlastalent.com. Interviews are by appointment only.
[SAG/AFTRA, NATR, ATA]

AVALON ARTISTS GROUP

5455 Wilshire Boulevard, Suite 900, Los Angeles, CA 90036
Telephone: 323-692-1700 **Fax:** 323-692-1722
Website: www.avalonartists.com
Departments and Staff:
President/Theatrical - Craig Holzberg;
Theatrical - Elmer Blanco;
Head of Youth Theatrical and Commercial - Candace Stewart;
Adult Commercial - Stephany Burns;
Ages Represented: All ages.
Details: This agency represents actors, models, broadcasters, singers, dancers, comedians, spokespersons, and hosts. They work in TV, film, commercials, voiceover, and industrials.
Tips: This agency accepts submissions only through mail. They attend showcases.
[SAG/AFTRA, NATR, AEA, ATA]

AVANT ARTISTS

4869 Topanga Canyon Boulevard, Suite 2,
Woodland Hiils, CA 91364
Telephone: 818-609-1556 **Website:** www.avantartists.com
E-Mail: info@avantartists.com
Ages Represented: All ages.
Details: Their departments include theatrical, commercial/print, voiceover, and youth.
Tips: Send on-camera submission via mail. Referrals can be sent via email. See website for detailed instructions. No phone calls, drop-offs, or walk-ins. They are currently seeking (1) youth of all enthicities (newborn-18) (2) editorial models, females 5'8" or taller, males 6'0" or taller (3) Asian-America, African-American, and Hispanic actors (bilingual talent is a plus).
[SAG/AFTRA]

AVO TALENT

5670 Wilshire Boulevard, #1930, Los Angeles, CA 90036
Telephone: 310-360-7680 **Website:** www.avotalent.com
E-Mail: info@avotalent.com
Departments and Staff:
    Principal - Sandie Schnarr;
    Principal - Peter Varano;
    Commercial Voiceover - Jerry Ryba;
    Commercial On-Camera - Wendy Morrison;
    Trailer/Promo/Narration - Brian J. Macon
Details: This agency represents voiceover artists and commercial actors.
Tips: This agency accepts headshotsand resumes by mail or email to wmorrison@avotalent.com. They accept voiceover submissions through Facebook only. Interviews by appointment only.
[SAG/AFTRA]

BAIER/KLEINMAN INTERNATIONAL

16917 Ventura Boulevard, #9, Encino, CA, 91316
Telephone: 818-781-3841 **E-Mail:** bki@anet.net
Departments and Staff:
    Owner/Agent - Joel Kleinman
Ages Represented: 18+
Details: This agency represents talent in theatre, film, and TV.
Tips: You can send submissions to this agency via email at bki@anet.net or by mail. Interviews by appointment only.
[SAG/AFTRA, AEA]

BARON ENTERTAINMENT

13848 Ventura Boulevard, #A, Sherman Oaks, CA 91423
Telephone: 323-969-1000 **Fax:** 818-933-0798
Website: www.baronentertainment.com
Departments and Staff:
    Owner/Agent - Theodore Richter;
    Executive Director/Lead Agent - Martin Herrera
Ages Represented: All ages.
Details: This agency is open to submissions from actors, models, variety artists, stuntspeople, and children.
Tips: Submit via mail, addressed to "ATTN: New Talent". Interviews by appointment only.
[SAG/AFTRA]

NOTES

BELLA AGENCY

1680 North Vine Street, Suite 714, Los Angeles, CA 90028
Telephone: 323-462-9191 **Website:** www.bellaagency.com
E-Mail: internla@bellaagency.com
Ages Represented: 18-65
Departments and Staff:
  Print Agent - Cheyenne Brink; Lauren Smith
  On-camera Agent - Taylor Hensley
  Assistant - Olivia Wilcox;
  President - Ray Volant
Ages Represented: 18+
Details: Bella Agency is a reputable bi-coastal model and talent agency looking to expand their roster in the Los Angeles office for adult commerical and print.
Tips: No calls or drop-offs. Commercial actors may submit their headshot and resume via email or through the Bella Agency website.
Model open calls for the print department occur every Tuesday from 2-3 PM. Height requirements are as follows: Women 5'6-5'10, Men 5'10-6'2. Picture and resume are strongly suggested; if you do not have professional photos, bring in a few snapshots. Photos will not be returned.
[SAG/AFTRA]

BERMAN/SACKS TALENT AGENCY

8335 Sunset Boulevard, Suite 225, West Hollywood, CA 90069
Telephone: 323-337-9033 **Website:** www.bermansacks.com
E-Mail: bermansacks@gmail.com
Ages Represented: 18+
Details: This agency represents actors for theatre, film/TV, and commercials.
Tips: They will accept email submissions of photo, resume, and demo link only. No hardcopies, phone calls, or drop-offs will be accepted.Send submissions to assistant@bermansaks.com for consideration.
[SAG/AFTRA, AEA]

BEVERLY AGENCY

9025 Wilshire Boulevard, Suite #301, Beverly Hills, CA 90211
Telephone: 310-601-7776 **Website:** www.beverlyagencyinc.com
E-Mail: agencyrep@gmail.com, submissions.beverlyagency@gmail.com

Departments and Staff:
    Owner/Agent - Beverly Graham
Ages Represented: 4+
Details: Founded in 1989, the Beverly Agency represents a diverse group of talent both locally and internationally. They represent adults, seniors, adolescents, and children (older than age 4) for print, TV, commercial, and film. Actors should have some form of improv training.
Tips: This agency will only accept submissions through their website; email submissions.beverlyagency@gmail.com.
[SAG/AFTRA]

BEVERLY HECHT AGENCY

6320 Canoga Avenue, Suite 1500, Woodland Hills, CA 91367
Telephone: 818-559-5600   **Fax:** 818-559-7485
Website: www.beverlyhecht.com
E-Mail: submissions@beverlyhecht.com
Departments and Staff:
    Owner/Agent - Teresa Valente
Ages Represented: 6+
Details: Beverly Hecht represents talent in TV, film, and print.
Tips: Submissions are accepted through mail or email.
[ATA, SAG/AFTRA]

BICOASTAL TALENT AND LITERARY AGENCY

2600 West Olive Ave, Suite 500, Burbank, CA 91505
Telephone: 818-845-0150   **Fax:** 818-845-0152
E-Mail: submissions@BiCoastaltalent.com
Website: www.bicoastaltalent.com
Departments and Staff:
    Owner/Commercial - Greta Hanley;
    Motion Pictures/TV/Literary - Liz Hanley;
    Youth Motion Pictures/TV - Niche Martin;
Ages Represented: All ages.
Details: This agency typically represents talent in TV, film, and commercials.
Tips: Submissions are only accepted through the mail, and adults must have union membership or eligibility.
[SAG/AFTRA, AEA, WGA]

BLAKE AGENCY, THE

23441 Malibu Colony Road, Malibu, CA 90265
Telephone: 310-456-2022   **Fax:** 310-456-9994
Website: www.theblakeagency.com

E-Mail: theblakeagency@gmail.com
Departments and Staff:
 Owner/Agent - Merritt Blake
Details: The Blake Agency represents established actors for commercials, theatre, film, and TV.
Tips: This agency accepts industry referrals only.
[SAG/AFTRA]

BLESICH SPORTS & ENTERTAINMENT, INC.

620 Newport Center Dr., Suite 1100, Newport Beach, CA 92660
Telephone: 301-702-8602 **Fax:** 310-702-8602
E-Mail: info@blesich.com
Departments and Staff:
 President/NBA and Talent Agent - Nick Blesich;
 Director of Operations - Jay Meyer
Details: This firm books sports personalities and actors for commercials, film, and TV.
Tips: Submit application materials by mail. Interviews are granted by appointment only.
SAG/AFTRA

BLOC TALENT AGENCY, INC.

6100 Wilshire Boulevard, Suite 1100, Los Angeles, CA 90048
Telephone: 323-954-7730 **Fax:** 323-954-7731
Website: www.blocagency.com
E-Mail: blocassistant@blocagency.com
Departments and Staff:
 Heads/Agents - Brendan Filuk, Laney Filuk;
 Talent Representative - Jennifer Musgrove Tanisha Whiting, Steve Gaeto;
 Assistant - Talia Kushynski
Details: This talent agency represents actors, choreographers, dancers, and extreme athletes. They book for film, episodic and commercial TV, live stage, theatre performances, industrials, music videos, and print.
Tips: They prefer referrals but they do accept photos and demos by mail. Applications can also be made on their website.
[SAG/AFTRA, AEA]

BROWN LEADER MANAGEMENT GROUP

23823 Malibu Road, Suite 50-120, Malibu, CA 90265
Telephone: 424-260-1127 or 310-456-6796

NOTES

Departments and Staff:
President - Phillip Leader;
VP - Patricia Brown; Creative Executive/Manager -
Jermaine Shelton
E-Mail: philip@brownleadergroup.com
Tips: Send headshot and resume by mail or email. Interviews by appointment only. No calls, no dropoffs.

BOBBY BALL TALENT AGENCY

3500 W Olive Avenue, Suite 300, Burbank, CA 91505
Telephone: 818-506-8188 **Fax:** 818-333-2950
Website: www.bbatalent.com **E-Mail:** info@bbatalent.com
Departments and Staff:
CEO - Renee Howard
Kids & Young Adult Commercial - Mike O'Dell;
Adult Commercial - Christine Tarello;
Ages Represented: All ages.
Details: This agency represents a wide variety of performers in all areas. They work with children and young adults.
Tips: Any of the agents can be emailed through the website, although mailed submissions are preferred. Voiceover and youth commercial submissions must be industry referrals.
[SAG/AFTRA, ATA, WGA]

BODY PARTS MODELS, INC.

2023 Coldwater Canyon Drive, Beverly Hills, CA 90210
Telephone: 310-275-8263 **Fax:** 310-273-5878
Website: www.bodypartsmodels.com
E-Mail: linda@bodypartsmodels.com
Departments and Staff: Agents - Linda Teglovic, Nikki Carson
Details: This agency represents adults, children, models, dancers, broadcasters, foreign/ethnic individuals, and musical artists in TV and commercials, mostly in a modeling capacity.
Tips: Calling, emailing, or mailing are acceptable means of contacting the agency.
[SAG/AFTRA]

BRADY, BRANNON, & RICH, LLC

5670 Wilshire Boulevard, #820, Los Angeles, CA 90036
Telephone: 323-852-9559 **Fax:** 323-852-9579
Website: www.bbrtalentagency.com
E-Mail: newtalent@bbrtalent.com

NOTES

Departments and Staff:
CEO - Stuart Robinson;
On Camera - Judy Rich, Pat Brannon, Jill Johnson,
Print - Jesse Perez;
Laura Bowman, Mark Masten, Grace Ameter;
Theatrical - Jodie Bowman, Alisa Taylor, Sylvia Brasuell;
Print - Laura Bowman, Bri Beck
Ages Represented: 18+
Details: They represent talent in TV, film, theatre, voiceover, commercials, and print.
Tips: In order to submit materials to this agency, send a medium resolution jpeg (nothing over 2MB), resume, and list any referrals you may have to: newtalent@bbrtalent.com (for commercials) and theatricalsubmissions@bbrtalent.com (for theatrical).
[SAG/AFTRA]

BRANDON'S COMMERCIALS UNLIMITED

190 N. Canon Drive, #208, Beverly Hills, CA 90210
Telephone: 310-278-5123   **Fax:** 310-278-4665
Website: www.commercialsunlimited.org
E-Mail: cu190@yahoo.com
Departments and Staff:
President - Sonjia Warren Brandon;
Senior Vice President - Randi Rubenstein;
CEO - Nora Zilz; Vice President - Paul R. Williams
Ages Represented: 4+
Details: Known for their solid on-camera, print, and voiceover success, Commercials Unlimited is a full-service agency offering expertise in celebrity endorsements, sports representation, soap opera talent, youth commercials, the Hispanic market, plus radio, and TV hosting.
Tips: To submit materials to this agency, send a (non-returnable) picture and resume to: Commercials Unlimited 190 N. Canon Dr. #208 Beverly Hills, CA 90210 ATTN: New Talent

BRESLER-KELLY & ASSOCIATES

11500 West Olympic Boulevard, #400, Los Angeles, CA 90064
Telephone: 310-479-5611
Departments and Staff:
Co-Owners - Sandy Bresler, John Kelly
Details: This agency represents actors for theatrical work, and represents writers. They are known for representing actor Jack Nicholson.

BROGAN AGENCY LLC, THE

1517 Park Row, Venice, CA 90291
Telephone: 310-450-9700 **Fax:** 310-450-9600
Website: www.thebroganagency.com
E-Mail: info@thebroganagency.com,
  newtalent@thebroganagency.com
Departments and Staff:
   Owner/Agent - Shawn Brogan;
   Children's Division - Faren Collins
Ages Represented: All ages.
Details: The Brogan Agency is a full service, exclusive talent agency representing all types and all ages. They also attend showcases and workshops.
Tips: Headshots accepted by mail or email. The agency will contact you to make an appointment..
[SAG/AFTRA, ATA, WGA]

BRS/GAGE

5757 Wilshire Boulevard, #659, Los Angeles, CA 90036
Telephone: 323-857-6666 **Website:** www.brsgage.com
E-Mail: brsgage@gmail.com
Departments and Staff:
Partners - David Shaul, Mark Redanty, Martin Gage
   Agents - Adam Lazarus, Evan Miller; Assistant - Craig
   Feblowitz;
   Office Assistant - Michael Schwartz
Details: This agency represents stage actors for plays and musicals, and on-camera actors for film and TV. They have offices in NY.
Tips: This agency accepts submissions by industry refferals only. No unsolicited materials are considered.
[ATA, SAG/AFTRA, AEA]

CARRY COMPANY, THE

3875 Wilshire Boulevard, # 402, Los Angeles, CA 90010
Telephone: 213-388-0770 **Website:** www.carrycompany.com
Departments and Staff:
   Owner - Sharon Carry;
   Assistant - Amanda Keith
Details: They represent talent of all ages for commercials, theatre, film, and TV.
[SAG/AFTRA, AEA, WGA]

NOTES

CASTLE HILL ENTERPRISES

1101 S Orlando Avenue, Los Angeles, CA 90035
Telephone: 323-653-3535   **Website:** www.castlehillagency.com
E-Mail: leigh@castlehillagency.com
Departments and Staff: Owner/Agent - Leigh Castle;
  Associate - Lisa Castle
Details: Along with their actors, they've booked everything from fire jugglers, mimes, belly dancers and magicians, to 40 piece orchestras, and, occasionally, animals!
[SAG/AFTRA, AEA]

CAVALERI & ASSOCIATES TALENT & LITERARY AGENCY

178 S. Victory Boulevard, Burbank, CA, 91502
Telephone: 818-955-9300   **Fax:** 818-955-9399
Departments and Staff:
  Owner/Theatrical - Ray Cavaleri;
  Commercial/Children Agent - Renae Bell;
  Literary Agent - Al Choi
Ages Represented: 6+
Details: This agency works with children through adults in commercials, TV, film, and literary. They also represent producers and directors.
Tips: Submissions are accepted by mail only. No walk-ins allowed.
[SAG/AFTRA, AEA, WGA, DGA]

CENTRAL ARTISTS

3308 W Burbank Boulevard, Burbank, CA 91505
Telephone: 818-557-8284   **Fax:** 818-557-8348
Website: www.centralartists.com
E-Mail: centralartists@centralartists.com
Departments and Staff:
  Owners - Laura Walsh, Jean-Marc Carre;
  Theatrical Assistant - Melony Begakis;
  Youth Talent Agent - Nicole Connor
Ages Represented: All ages.
Details: Over the years this agency has represented actors for feature films, TV series, national commercials, and print ad campaigns. They also represent little people and children.
Tips: For this agency, you may submit your material to submissions@centralartists.com or mail in your materials.

CHEZCHIC TALENT

9663 Santa Monica Boulevard, #5000, Beverly Hills, CA 90210
Telephone: 888-989-2442 **Website:** www.chezchictalent.com
E-Mail: info@chezchictalent.com
Departments and Staff:
 Owner/Agent - Brett Vance
Ages Represented: 16-30
Details: This agency works in the fashion and entertainment industry, providing a great opportunity for actors to build a portfolio, even if they are unfamiliar with the fashion and entertainment industry. ChezChic will represent an individual for both modeling and acting in areas of runway, print, film, and TV. They also have a hosting division.
Tips: Interested applicants can apply through the submissions page on the company website.

CHIC MODELS

5150 East PCH, Suite. 200, Long Beach, CA 90804
Telephone: 562-433-8097 **Website:** www.chicmodels.com
E-Mail: info@chicmodels.com
Details: This Agency represents actors for commercial print or TV commercials. In the modeling business since 1988, Chic Models boasts top retail and fashion clients such as Disney, ASICS, P&G (Wella, Clairol, Sebastian, etc.,) L'Oreal (Matrix, Pureology, Logics,
Tips: See the "Become a model" page on the agency website for height and size requirements.
[SAG/AFTRA]

CIRCLE TALENT ASSOCIATES

401 Wilshire Boulevard, 12th Floor, Santa Monica, CA 90401
Telephone: 310-496-4501 **Website:** www.circletalent.com
E-Mail: info@circletalent.com
Departments and Staff:
 President/Agent - Jennifer Lee Garland
Details: Circle Talent negotiates bookings for national network commercials, roles on TV series, and roles for films ranging from independent features to studio blockbusters.
Tips: Submit headshots, resumes, and other materials to this agency through their website.
[ATA]

NOTES

CLEAR TALENT GROUP

10950 Ventura Boulevard, Studio City, CA 91604
Telephone: 818-509-0121 **Fax:** 818-509-7729
Website: www.cleartalentgroup.com
E-Mail: lainfo@cleartalentgroup.com
Departments and Staff:
    Owner/President - Tim O'Brien;
    VP - Brianna Ancel;
    Youth Department - Bonnie Ventis, Jody Alexander;
    Agents - Philip Marcus, Allison Sweeney, Shayna Brouilard
Details: Departments include theatrical, dance, commercial/print, voiceover, and young people.
Tips: Each department has its own submission policy. See website for specifics or email lainfo@cleartalentgroup.com.
[SAG/AFTRA, AEA, ATA]

COAST TO COAST TALENT

3350 Barham Boulevard, Los Angeles, CA 90068
Telephone: 323-845-9200 **Fax:** 323-845-9212
Website: www.ctctalent.com
Departments and Staff:
    President - Jeremiah Doryon
    CFO - Elyah Doryon;
    Adults, Commercials/Celebrity Athletes - Hugh Leon;
    Youth Division - Meredith Fine
Details: This agency has divisions in print, theatre, commercials, pro sports, voiceover, and youth.
Tips: Submit headshots and resumes to this agency by mail only.
[DGA, WGA, ATA, SAG/AFTRA]

COLLEEN CLER AGENCY

178 S Victory Boulevard, #108, Burbank, CA 91502
Telephone: 818-841-7943 **Fax:** 818-841-4541
Website: www.colleencler.com
E-Mail: newtalent@colleencler.com
Departments and Staff:
    Owner/Agent - Colleen Cler
Ages Represented: All ages.
Details: This agency represents talent of all ages in print and commercials.
Tips: To be considered for representation, send a current snapshot and a way to contact you via email or mail with "ATTN: New Talent." Interviews are by appointment only.
[SAG/AFTRA]

COMMERCIAL TALENT, INC.

12711 Ventura Boulevard, #285, Studio City, CA 91604
Telephone: 818-505-1431 **Fax:** 818-579-4753
Website: www.commercialtalentagency.com
Departments and Staff:
    Owners/Agents - Sheila Di Marco, Neil Kreppel;
    Agents - Blair Taylor, Arlene Glucksman, Paul Barrutia;
    Assistants - Alicia Beekman, Nathan Higgins
Ages Represented: 3+
Details: The departments of this agency include: commercial, hosting/alternative TV, direct response/infomercial, and print.
Tips: To submit materials to this agency, send resumes and headshots via mail only.
[ATA, SAG/AFTRA, AEA]

CONNOR ANKRUM AND ASSOCIATES

1680 N. Vine Street, Suite 1016, Hollywood, CA 90028
Telephone: 323-463-8355
E-Mail: erin@connorankrum.com
Departments and Staff:
    Partners/Agents - David Ankrum, Erin Connor;
    Agents - Caleigh Vancata, Steve Walker, Steven Dry,
    Stephanie Hoover
Ages Represented: 18-64
Details: This agency represents established actors in all main areas.
Tips: Submissions are accepted through mail only.
[SAG/AFTRA, AEA, WGA]

CORSA AGENCY

11704 Wilshrie Boulevard, #204, Los Angeles, CA 90025
Telephone: 310-231-7010,
E-Mail: larry@corsaagency.com, thomas@corsaagency.com
Departments and Staff:
    Owner - Larry Corsa;
    Associate - Thomas Richards
Ages Represented: 13-64
Details: This agency represents talent for film and TV.
Tips: They ask that materials be submitted by mail only.
[ATA]

NOTES

CR KIDS

256 S Robertson Boulevard, #888, Los Angeles, CA 90211
Telephone: 323-801-2190 **Website:** www.crkidstalent.com
E-Mail: cyndee@crkidstalent.com
Departments and Staff:
 Owner/Agent - Cyndee Romley
Ages Represented: 0-18
Details: CR Kids Talent has been guiding the careers of children in film, TV, commercials, and print.
Tips: Submit to this agency through their website.

CREATIVE ARTISTS AGENCY

2000 Avenue of the Stars, Los Angeles, CA 90067
Telephone: 424-288-2000 **Fax:** 424-288-2900
Website: www.caa.com **E-Mail:** info@caa.com
Departments and Staff:
 President - Richard Lovett;
 Partners - David O'Connor, Kevin Huvane, Bryan Lourd;
 Legit - George Lane; TV - Steven Lafferty;
 Motion Picture - Tracy Brennan, Jimmy Darmody, Joel Lubin, Jim Toth; Music - Rob Light; Commercials - Christian Carino;
Details: This is a top five agency. CAA represents performers, writers, and speakers over a wide assortment of disciplines, including broadcast, film, TV, theatre, voiceovers, commercials, and publishing with offices on the east coast.
Tips: Industry referrals only. No submissions.
[SAG/AFTRA, AEA, ATA, DGA]

CULBERTSON GROUP

9107 Wilshire Blvd., #450
Beverly Hills, CA 90210
Telephone: 323-650-9454
E-Mail: culbertsongroup@gmail.com
Departments and Staff:
 Partner/Commercial - Lorri Herman
 Partner/Theatrical - Eddie Culbertson
Details: This agency represents talent for theatre, film, TV, and commercials.
Tips: This agency accepts submissions (headshot, resume, demo reel) by email only.
[ATA, SAG/AFTRA]

CUNNINGHAM ESCOTT SLEVIN DOHERTY

10635 Santa Monica Boulevard, Suite 130, Los Angeles, CA 90025
Telephone: 310-475-2111   **Website:** www.cesdtalent.com
E-Mail: info@cesdtalent.com
Departments and Staff:
    President - Ken Slevin;
    Sr. VPs - David Ziff, Carol Scott, Mitchell Gossett;
    Secretary/Treasurer - Paul Doherty
Ages Represented: All ages.
Details: CESD has been representing talent across all media for decades. Adults and children are represented in voiceover, TV, film, print, fashion, and commercials. There is also a youth theatrical department.
Tips: They consider performers when submitted through the mail. If submitting for voiceover work, send through email as links to a personal or FTP website.
[SAG/AFTRA, AEA, ATA]

DPN - DANIA, PANARO, & NIST, INC.

9201 W Olympic Boulevard, Beverly Hills, CA 90212
Telephone: 310-432-7800   **Fax:** 310-432-7801
Website: www.dpntalent.com   **E-Mail:** info@dpntalent.com
Departments and Staff:
    President - Jeff Danis;
    Agents - Jennifer York, Max Mehlman, David Salazar,
    Brooke Barnett
Details: DPN works in voiceover, puppetry, on-camera appearances, and celebrity endorsements.
Tips: Submissions should be sent through email only.
[SAG/AFTRA]

DANIEL HOFF TALENT AGENCY

5455 Wilshire Boulevard, Suite 1100, Los Angeles, CA 90036
Telephone: 323-932-2500   **Fax:** 323-932-2501
Website: www.danielhoffagency.com
E-Mail: dave@danielhoffagency.com
Departments and Staff:
    Commercial/Print - Anna Leigh Simmons, Jessica Franklin,
    Garrett Hershey, Laura LaCombe;
    Musical Theatre - Dave Secor, Jeremy Sickles
    Film/Television - Kevin Turner, Dave Secor, David Arrigotti,

NOTES

Anna Leigh Simmons;
Musicians - Laura LaCombe;
Sports (Commerical, TV, Film, Print, Appearances) - Garrett Hershey;
Dance - Jessica Franklin;
Youth (Commerical, TV, Film, Print) - Ninna Sexsmith
Ages Represented: All ages.
Details: Actors are represented in commercials, print, theatrical, and film. They have a youth department.
Tips: Submissions by email only. Visit the website for more information.

DAVID SHAPIRA & ASSOCIATES

193 N Robertson Boulevard, Beverly Hills, CA 90211
Telephone: 310-967-0480 **Fax:** 310-659-4177
Website: dsa-comedy.com **E-Mail:** kk@dsa-agency.com
Departments and Staff:
Owner - David Shapira;
Agents - Mark Scroggs, Susan Fincham
Ages Represented: 18+
Details: DSA accepts adult actors for TV, film, commercials, voiceover, and broadcast journalism.
Tips: Email submissions are acceptable, and interview appointments can be made.
[SAG/AFTRA, WGA, DGA, ATA]

DDO ARTISTS

4605 Lankershim Boulevard, #340, North Hollywood, CA 91602
Telephone: 323-462-8000 **Fax:** 323-462-0100
Website: www.ddoagency.com
E-Mail: reception@ddoagency.com
Departments and Staff:
Partner - Bill Bohl;
Partner/Agency Director- Abigail Girvin
Partner/Adult Commercials Agent- Marlene Sutton;
Kids Agent- Laura Thede
Adult Commercial Agent- Julie Gudz, Rai Flynn
Stage Theatrical Agent- Anthony Boyer
Ages Represented: 4+
Details: Founded in 1969 by Dorothy Day Otis, DDO has focused on representing young talent.In their west coast offices they represent dancers and choreographers ages 8-90.
Tips: They take submissions from all ages through mail, and email submissions for dance and choreography can be sent to Lyndsay@ddoagency.com.
[SAG/AFTRA, AEA]

DEFINING ARTISTS, INC.

193 N. Robertson Boulevard, Beverly Hills, CA 90211
Telephone: 424-302-0073 **Fax:** 424-302-0763
Website: www.definingartists.com
E-Mail: info@definingartists.com
Departments and Staff:
   Owners/Agents - Kim Dorr-Tilley, Dede Binder;
   Partner/Agent - Breanna Bell
Ages Represented: 13-64
Details: This agency represents talent in film and TV.
Tips: Headshot, resume, and demo reel submissions accepted via email to definingartists@yahoo.com.
[ATA, SAG/AFTRA]

DON BUCHWALD & ASSOCIATES

6500 Wilshire Boulevard, Suite 2200, Los Angeles, CA 90048
Telephone: 323-655-7400 **Website:** www.buchwald.com
E-Mail: info@buckwald.com
Departments and Staff:
   President/CEO/Agent - Don Buchwald;
   COO - Richard Basch;
   VPs/Agents - Ricki Olshan, Robyn Stecher, Stephen Fisher;
   Broadcast Agent- David Swift
   Talent Agents- Cynthia Booth, Michael Carr, Gordon Macdonald, Angelo Padilla, Hannah Roth, Tim Scally, Bryan Walsh
   Young Talent Agent- Tim Weissan
Ages Represented: 2+
Details: This is a top ten agency. On both coasts, Don Buchwald represents actors for commercials, broadcast, film, TV, theatre, literary, youth,and beauty.
Tips: Mail submissions are preferred. For new client information please email btginfo@bbrtalent.com.
[SAG/AFTRA, AEA, WGA, DGA, ATA]

ELECTRA STAR MANAGEMENT

9229 Sunset Boulevard, #415, West Hollywood, CA 90069
Telephone: 310-943-1000 **Fax:** 310-25-3150
Website: www.electrastarmgmt.com
Departments and Staff:
   President - Michael Blakey;
   Executive Vice President - Drew Edwards;
   A&R Consultant - Jorge Hernandez;
   Talent Manager - Tom Bixby;

NOTES

Senior Project Manager - Bradley R. Peterson;
Project Manager, Graphic Designer, Executive Assistant -
Katya Shalayeva;
Details: Electra Star Management represents film and TV actors
as well as comedians and musicians. They also have an office in
Atlanta, GA.
Tips: This agency can be reached via their website or by mail.

ELITE MODEL MANAGEMENT & TALENT

345 North Maple Drive, Suite 176, Beverly Hills, CA 90210
Telephone:310-274-9395 **Fax:** 310-278-7520
Website: www.elitemodel.com **E-Mail:** LAinfo@elitemodel.com
Ages Represented: 16+
Details: This agency almost solely represents models, for print,
runway, and other spots. They also have offices in New York,
Miami, and Toronto.
Tips: Submit via wesbite.

ELLIS TALENT GROUP

4705 Laurel Canyon Boulevard, #300, Valley Village, CA 91607
Telephone: 818-980-8072   **Website:** www.ellistalentgroup.com
Departments and Staff:
    President/Agent - Pamala Ellis-Evenas;
    Agent - Gabrielle Allabashi
Details: This agency represents talent for film and TV. They also
work with comedians.
Tips: This agency accepts new talent via industry referral only.
Unsolicited materials are not considered.
[SAG/AFTRA, AEA]

ENVY LOS ANGELES

489 S Robertson Boulevard, #104A, Beverly Hills, CA 90211
Telephone: 310-694-8567
Website: www.envymodelmanagement.com
E-Mail: envyla@envymodelmanagement.com
Departments and Staff:
    President/Owner/Kids Theatrical - Daniel Mahan;
    Adult Theatrical - Jessica Chung;
    Men's Print/Runway - Marq Mendez;
    Women's Print/Runway - Jasmine Nicole;
    Commercials - Edgar Alvarez;
    Agents - Daniel Mahan, Edgar Alveraz, Branden Pitcher

Ages Represented: All ages.
Details: This agency represents talent for film, TV, and commercials.
Tips: Subit materials via email to: envyla@ envymodelmanagement.com. Phone calls and walk-ins are allowed.
[SAG/AFTRA]

FAME TALENT AGENCY

1441 N McCadden Place, Los Angeles, CA 90028
Telephone: 323-240-5566
E-Mail: fametalentagency@gmail.com
Departments and Staff:
    Owner/Agent - Whami Hwang;
    Agent - Mario Pacheco; Kids Deptartment - Sharlean Peck
Details: This agency represents talent for commercials, film, and TV
Tips: This agency accepts materials via mail only
[SAG/AFTRA]

FILM ARTISTS ASSOCIATES

21044 Ventura Boulevard, Suite 215, Woodland Hills, CA 91364
Telephone: 818-883-5008   **Fax:** 818-883-5040
Departments and Staff:
    President- Penrod Dennis
    CEO/Agent - Cris Dennis
Ages Represented: 18-64
Details: They represent actors in TV, film, print, and commercials.
Tips: Only submit through mail and do not send tapes unless requested.
[SAG/AFTRA]

FLICK EAST WEST TALENT

9200 Sunset Boulevard, #820 , West Hollywood, CA 90069
Telephone: 310-271-9111   **Fax:** 310-858-1701
Website: www.flickcommercials.com
E-Mail: info@flickcommercials.com
Departments and Staff:
    Director - Tina Kiratsoulis;
    Agents - Chris Bonk, Mike Colby
Details: This agency represents talent for commercials.
Tips: Flick accepts headshots and resumes by mail only. Interviews are by appointment only.
[SAG/AFTRA]

NOTES

FORD MODELS

9200 W Sunset Boulevard, #805, West Hollywood, CA 90069
Telephone: 310-276-8100
Website: www.models.fordmodels.com
Ages Represented: Female: 12-25, Male: 15+
Details: This agency represents models for print and runway, only. They also have offices in New York, Chicago, and Miami.
Tips: This agency accepts materials via mail or email.

FRED R. PRICE LITERARY-TALENT AGENCY

14044 Ventura Boulevard, 201, Sherman Oaks, CA 91423
Telephone: 818-763-6365
Details: Represents actors for theatre and commercial work.

GAGE GROUP

14724 Ventura Boulevard, #505, Sherman Oaks, CA 91403
Telephone: 818-905-3800 **E-Mail:** gagegroupla@gmail.com
Departments and Staff:
    Principal/Talent/Literary - Martin Gage;
    Commercials - Mark Fadness, Carol Elsner;
    Talent - Gerry Koch, Kitty McMillan, Arthur Toretzky, Judith Moss;
    Assistants - Madison Elsner, Madison Berrones
Details: This is a full service agency which represents actors for all media, writers, comedians, dancers, etc.
Tips: This agency accepts headshots and resumes via mail or email. They do not consider unsolicited scripts or demos.

GAR LESTER AGENCY (GLA)

11026 Ventura Boulevard, Suite 10, Studio City, CA 91604
Telephone: 818-769-1400 **Website:** www.glatalent.com
E-Mail: info@glatalent.com
Departments and Staff:
    Owner/Agent - Gar Lester;
    Assistant - David Lester
Ages Represented: 2+
Details: The Gar Lester Agency calls themselves one of the premiere boutique theatrical and commercial agencies in the country. They book a wide roster of talent in TV, commercial, and film.
Tips: This agency accepts headshots and resumes by mail only.

GERSH AGENCY

9465 Wilshire Boulevard, 6th Floor, Beverly Hills, CA 90212
Telephone: 310-274-6611 **Fax:** 310-274-3923
Website: www.gershagency.com **E-Mail:** info@gershla.com
Departments and Staff:
  Co-President/Talent - Bob Gersh;
  Co-President/Literary - David Gersh;
  Sr. Managing Partner/Co-Head, Talent - Leslie Siebert;
  Sr. Partner/Sr. Executive VP, Comedy/Personal Appearance
  - Rick Greenstein;
  Partner/Co-Head, Talent - David DeCamillo;
  Partner/Co-Head, TV Literary - Jack Dytman;
  Partner/Head, Film Financing & Packaging - Jay Cohen;
  Partner/Co-Head, Literary - Bayard Maybank;
  CFO - Jennifer Kullmann
Details: This is a top ten agency. They are a full service agency, representing talent for TV, film, commercials, theatre, special events, and more. They also have a New York office.
Tips: This agency only accepts new talent via industry referral, and does not consider any unsolicited materials
[SAG/AFTRA, WGA, ATA, AEA, AFM, DGA]

GLICK AGENCY, LLC, THE

1321 7th Street, #203, Santa Monica, CA 90401
Telephone: 310-593-6500 **Fax:** 310-593-6505
E-Mail: glickoffice@glickagency.com
Departments and Staff:
  Agents - Steve Glick, Fred Whitehead, Barbara Pollans,
  Amy Abell; Executive Assistant - Leia Vincent
Details: This agency represents talent for film, commercials, TV, theatre, and also screenwriters, directors and producers.
Tips: No calls or drop-offs; industry referrals only.
[SAG/AFTRA, ATA]

GLOBAL ARTISTS AGENCY

6253 Hollywood Boulevard, #508, Los Angeles, CA 90028
Telephone: 323-836-0320 **Fax:** 323-836-0325
Website: globalartistsagency.net
E-Mail: info@globalartistsagency.net
Departments and Staff:
  Agents - April Lim, Monica Barkett, Cynthia Booth,
  Todd Maginn,Johnathan Silverman
Ages Represented: 2-64

NOTES

Details: This agency represents talent for film, TV, commercials, hosting/special events, as well as a variety of other media.
Tips: This agency accepts new talent from industry referrals only; unsolicited materials are not considered.
[SAG/AFTRA, ATA]

GO 2 TALENT AGENCY, INC.

2825 W Magnolia Boulevard, Burbank, CA 91505
Telephone: 818-843-9800 **Fax:** 818-843-9801
Website: www.gototalentagency.com
E-Mail: info@go2talentagency.com
Departments and Staff:
    President - Jerry Lindholm;
    VP - Lisa Lindholm
Details: Their focus is dancers encompassing all fields in the industry, including TV, film, commercials, print, music videos, and theatre.
Tips: Submissions can be made to newtalent@go2talentagency.com; agency holds audition twice ayear in LA.
[SAG/AFTRA, ATA, AEA]

GRACE MODEL MANAGEMENT

12400 Ventura Boulevard, #421, Studio City, CA 91604
Telephone: 323-590-9919 **Fax:** 323-590-9919
E-Mail: info@gracemodelmanagement.com,
      grace@gracemodelmanagement.com
Details: This agency focuses on model management, for print and runway and other spots.
Tips: This agency accepts submissions via email to submission@gracemodelmanagement.com. They require a headshot profile, a bodyshot, a face shot, and all relevant body information and contact info.

GSK & ASSOCIATES

6399 Wilshire Boulevard, Suite 415, Los Angeles, CA 90048
Telephone: 323-782-1654 **Fax:** 323-345-5690
Website: www.gsktalent.com
E-Mail: contact@gsktalent.com
Departments and Staff:
    Partner/Agent, Below-the-Line - Ivana Savic
    Partner/Agent, Below-the-Line/Literary - Susan Grant
    Agent, Talent - Larry Metzger
Details: GSK Talent has a theatrical an literary division. They also represent line producers, directors of photography, production

designers, assistant directors, costume designers, editors, sound mixers and visual effects supervisors.
Tips: They can be contacted via email or phone.
[SAG/AFTRA, DGA, WGA]

GVA TALENT
(GREATER VISION ARTISTS)

8981 Sunset Boulevard, Suite 204, Los Angeles, CA 90036
Telephone: 310-278-1310 **Fax:** 310-888-1290
Website: gvatalent.com **E-Mail:** gvagecko@aol.com
Departments and Staff:
    Theatrical/Owner - Geneva V. Bray;
    Theatrical/TV - Tony Martinez, Gwenn Pepper;
    Assistant - Jill Carmen Lukk, Nicholas Virga
Ages Represented: 18-64
Details: This agency represents talent for work in TV, film, and theatre, as well as screenwriters, directors, and hosts/MCs.
Tips: Referrals only.
[SAG/AFTRA]

H. DAVID MOSS & ASSOCIATES

6063 Vineland Avenue, N. Hollywood, CA, 91606
Telephone: 323-465-1234 **Fax:** 323-465-1241
Departments and Staff:
    Owner/President - H. David Moss;
    Assistants - Ryan Angel, Laura Buckles
Ages Represented: 13+
Details: Actors of all types across represented for theatre, film, TV, industrials, and print.
Tips: Mail submissions only.
[SAG/AFTRA, AEA, AGVA, DGA, WGA]

HANLON TALENT

6399 Wilshire Boulevard, #709, Los Angeles, CA 90048
Telephone: 323-951-1181 **Website:** www.hanlontalent.com
E-Mail: court@hanlontalent.com
Departments and Staff:
    Owner/Agent - Courtney Hanlon;
    Youth Division - Sherree Hanlon
Details: This agency represents adult talent for commercials, and youth talent for commercials and theatre.
Tips: Hanlon Talent accepts submissions by mail or email. Indicate "Agency Representation" on the envelope or in the subject line.
[SAG/AFTRA]

NOTES

HAPPEN AGENCY, THE

9795 Cabrini Drive, Burbank, CA, 91504
Telephone: 818-588-6437
Website: www.thehappenagency.com
E-Mail: randi@thehappenagency.com;
shaunna@thehappenagency.com
Departments and Staff:
    Theatrical- Randi Bergsma
    Commercial- Shaunna Griffith
Ages Represented: 18 +
Details: This agency has a theatrical department and commercials department.
Tips: Talent submissions are accepted via a form on the webiste.
[SAG/AFTRA, NON-UNION]

HOLLANDER TALENT GROUP

14011 Ventura Boulevard, #202, Sherman Oaks, CA 91423
Telephone: 818-382-9800   **Website:** www.hollandertalent.com
E-Mail: vivian@hollandertalent.com
Departments and Staff:
    Agents - Vivian Hollander, Stefane Wetherhold
Ages Represented: 0-18
Details: Established in 1996 and committed to catering to young performers, Hollander Talent Group Children works with actors between the ages of 0-18. Children of all ethnicities are represented in commercials, TV, film, and voiceover.
Tips: Photos and resumes are preferred, via email or mail. They do not want voiceover demos or videos. Interviews by appointment only.
[SAG/AFTRA]

HOLLYWOOD ORIGINAL TALENT

6115 Selma Ave. #207, Los Angeles, CA 90028
Telephone: 323-460-2951
E-Mail: hollywoodoriginaltalent@gmail.com
Departments and Staff:
    President/Agent - Lisa Butler
Details: This agency represents talent of all ages for commercials, theatre, film, and TV
Tips: Submit photo, resume, cover letter, and link to work via email or mail.
[SAG/AFTRA]

HOLLYWOOD SELECT TALENT AGENCY

6408 Selma Avenue, Los Angeles, CA 90028
Telephone: 323-871-1240
E-Mail: info@hollywoodselecttalent.com
Details: Represents actors and models for print.
Tips: Photos and measurements can be submitted through the agency website.

HOUSE OF REPRESENTATIVES, THE

1434 6th Street, #1, Santa Monica, CA 90401
Telephone: 310-451-2345 **E-Mail:** agents@thehouseofreps.com
Departments and Staff:
　　Agents - Pam Braverman, Denny Sevier;
　　Commercial - Indra Armstrong Clark, Aurora Lizardi,
　　Rebecca Morgan; Theatrical - Claudine Vacca
Details: This agency represents talent of all ages for commercials, theatre, film, and TV.
Tips: Submissions are accepted by mail. Please do not send your materials to more than one agent. Interviews are held by appointment only.
[DGA, ATA]

HOWARD TALENT WEST AGENCY

17000 Ventura Blvd., Suite 210, Encino, CA 91316
Telephone: 818-766-530
Website: www.howardtalentwestagency.com
Departments and Staff:
　　Owner/Agent/Theatrical - Bonnie Howard;
　　Print/Commercials - Lynn Eriks
Details: This exclusive agency represents actors of all ages and types in TV, film, print, commercials and Equity. They also represent martial artists and stunts.
Tips: Submit to bonniehoward@howardtalentwest.met for Theatrical or lynnerik@howardtalentwest.net for Commercials. If you submit by mail do not seal envelopes or send unsolicited tapes. If you submit by email only submit links, do not attach files. No drop-offs will be considered. Interviews by appointment only.
[SAG/AFTRA, AEA, DGA,]

HRI

100 Universal City Plaza, Bungalo 7152, Universal City, CA 91608
Telephone: 818-733-2424 **Fax:** 818-733-4307
E-Mail: assistant@hritalent.com
Departments and Staff:
    Owner/Commercial - Michelle J. Henderson;
    Director/Theatrical - Tanya Kleckner;
    Commercial - Donna Kim;
    Assistant/Theatrical - Mary Conklin
Details: Represents talent of all ages for print, film, and TV, celebrity campaigns, and brand marketing
Tips: Submissions are accepted by mail only. Interviews by appointment only.
[SAG/AFTRA]

IMG BROADCASTING

2049 Century Park East, #2480, Century City, CA 90067
Telephone: 424-653-1960 **Website:** www.imgworld.com
Departments and Staff:
    VP - Babette Perry;
    Managers - Chris Kettler, Dan O'Connor;
    Client Services - Jazmin Machado
Details: Represents talent for print, broadcast journalism, fashion, and sports personalities.
[SAG/AFTRA]

IMPERIUM 7, LLC

5455 Wilshire Boulevard, #1706, Los Angeles, CA 90036
Telephone: 323-931-9099 **Fax:** 323-931-9084
Website: www.imperium-7.com **E-Mail:** info@imperium-7.com
Departments and Staff:
    Theatrical Agent - Steven Neibert;
    Commercial Agent - Tracy Mapes;
    Commercial Assistant - Jake Miller
    Voiceover Agents - Nick Carreras, Marni Anhalt;
Details: Actors of all ages are represented in TV, film, comedy, commercials, theatre, and voiceovers.
Tips: Submissions are accepted by mail or email. If submitting by email submit links only, not attachments. Send any inquries to admin@imperium-7.com.
[SAG/AFTRA, ATA]

INDEPENDENT ARTISTS AGENCY

9601 Wilshire Boulevard, #750, Beverly Hills, CA 90210
Telephone: 310-550-5000
Departments and Staff:
    President/Celebrity/On-Camera/Voiceover - Laura
    Fogelman;
    Sr. VP/Celebrity/On-Camera/Voiceover - Beverly Kline;
    Assistant - Jessica Ellis
Tips: This agency only accepts industry referrals. They do not accept unsolicited submissions.
[SAG/AFTRA]

INFINITE TALENT AGENCY

15206 Ventura Boulevard, # 214, Sherman Oaks, CA 91403
Telephone: 818-817-7598
Departments and Staff:
    Agents - Sharon Rose, Thadeus, Tania Ko
Details: This agency represents talent of all ages for theatre, commercial, and print.
Tips: Submissions are accepted by mail or by email. However, they only accept adult theatrical submissions through industry referral only. Include "ATTN: New Talent" with submissions. No in person drop-offs will be accepted.
[SAG/AFTRA]

INNOVATIVE ARTISTS

1505 10th Street, Santa Monica, CA 90401
Telephone: 310-656-0400   **Fax:** 310-665-0456
Website: www.innovativeartists.com   **E-Mail:** talent@iala.com
Departments and Staff:
    President - Scott Harris;
    Executive VP - Nevin Dolcefino;
    VPS - Debbie Haeusler, Jonathan Howard, Marcia Hurwitz,
    Maury DiMauro, Gary Gersh
Details: This is a top ten agency. Founded in 1982, this agency has expanded into TV, film, theatre, voiceover, commercials, beauty, literary, branding, hosting, and digital media, establishing a firm reputation in Los Angeles, New York, and Chicago.
Tips: Submissions can be made by industry referral only.
[DGA, WGA, ATA, SAG/AFTRA, AEA]

NOTES

ICM PARTNERS

10250 Constellation Boulevard, Los Angeles, CA 90067
Telephone: 310-550-4000   **Fax:** 310-550-4055
Website: www.icmpartners.com
E-Mail: careersla@icmpartners.com
Departments and Staff:
    Partners - Dan Baime, Lorrie Bartlett, Bonnie Bernstein, John Burnham, Ted Chevrin, Carter Cohn, Harley Copen, Kris Dahl, Kevin Crotty, Dan Donohue, Carol Goll, Mark Gordon, Hildy Gottlieb, Sloan Harris, Patrick Herold, Paul Hook, Toni Howard, Chuck James, Jenn Joel, Michael Kagan, Steve Levine, Richard Levy, Greg Lipstone, Doug MacLaren, Brian Mann, Esther Newberg, Janet Carol Norton, Dar Rollins, Adam Schweitzer, Mark Siegel, Chris Silbermann, Chris Smith, Amanda Urban, Chris von Goetz, Bart Walker, Joanne Wiles, Eddy Yablans, Lori York
Details: ICM Partners is one of the world's largest talent and literary agencies, with offices in Los Angeles, New York, Washington, D.C. and London. A cornerstone of the entertainment industry for more than three decades, ICM Partners represents creative and technical talent in the fields of motion pictures, television, music, publishing, live performance, branded entertainment and new media. Under the leadership of partners from each of the agency's core areas of business, ICM Partners continues actively to seek new opportunities for its clients as emerging technologies reshape the media landscape.
Tips: This agency only accepts industry referrals. Unsolicited submissions will not be accepted.
[AFM, DGA, WGA, ATA, AGVA, AFTRA, AEA]

INTERNATIONAL MODELS AND TALENT AGENCY

1901 Avenue of the Stars, #200, Century City, CA 90067
Telephone: 310-4611-550   **Website:** www.imta.com
Ages Represented: 4+
Details: IMTA was established in 1987 with the goal of creating an organization which helps training centers and agencies find new talent. Every year they host a five-day convention in New York and in Los Angeles where actors, dancers, singers, models, and songwriters can demonstrate their talent. These competitions also include award events, seminars, and callback/interview opporunities with agents and scouts.
Tips: This agency's website lists agencies around the world affiliated with IMTA. Talent must be a part of these studios or

agencies in order to be considered for an IMTA competition. IMTA can be contacted through their website.

IRV SCHECHTER

9460 Wilshire Boulevard, Suite 300, Beverly Hills, CA 90212
Telephone: 310-278-8070
E-Mail: asst@isagency.com
Details: This agency represents writers and directors only. Industry referral only.
[DGA, WGA, ATA, SAG/AFTRA, AEA]

JACK LIPPMAN AGENCY

9151 Sunset Boulevard, West Hollywood, CA 90069
Telephone: 310-276-5677 **Fax:** 310-276-2559
Website: www.jlatalent.com
E-Mail: modelsubmissions@jlatalent.com
Departments and Staff:
    Founders - Jack Lippman, Kendall Park;
    Agents - Nic de Armendi, Sumer Stamper
Details: JLA Talent was established by childhood friends Jack Lippman and Kendall Park. They are a full service talent agency that handles commercial, print, TV, film, and theatre.
[SAG/AFTRA]

JANA LUKER AGENCY

1923 1/2 Westwood Boulevard, Suite 3, Los Angeles, CA 90025
Telephone: 310-441-2822 **Fax:** 310-441-2823
Departments and Staff:
    Agents - Jana Luker, Kathy Keeley, Amy Luker
Ages Represented: 2+
Details: A small agency that represents performers age 4 and up, especially kids, teens, and young adults.
Tips: Talent should submit via mail. Children submissions may be emailed to amyluker@roadrunner.com.
[SAG/AFTRA, AEA, WGA]

JENNY STRICKLIN TALENT AGENCY (JSTA)

178 S Victory Boulevard, Suite 106, Burbank, CA 91502
Telephone: 747-477-1400 **Fax:** 747-477-1405
Website: jstalentagency.com
Departments and Staff:
    Owner/Agent – Jenny Stricklin
    Agent – Eric Stevens

Details: Jenny Stricklin Talent Agency (JSTA) is a full- service licensed and bonded, commercial and theatrical agency. We represent adults and children in the areas of on-camera commercial, print commercial, TV, and motion pictures.

Tips: Submissions accepted by regular mail or email. Interviews by appointment only. No calls or visits – please. Open Calls are held the first Thursday of the month between the hours of 3- 6 pm

[SAG/AFTRA]

JERRY PACE AGENCY, THE

120 S Victory Boulevard, #205, Burbank, CA 91502
Telephone: 818-783-4890 **Fax:** 818-501-8857
Website: www.jerrypaceagency.com
E-Mail: info@jerrypaceagency.com
Departments and Staff:
    Owner/Film and TV - Jerry Pace;
    Commercials and Print - Laurie Morgan, Pamela Woodson
Details: They represent talent of all ages for commercials, theatre, film, and TV.
Tips: Submit applications by mail or email. Interviews will be granted by appointment only.
[AGA, SAG/AFTRA, AEA]

JFA JAIME FERRAR AGENCY

4741 Laurel Canyon Boulevard, #110, Valley Village, CA 91607
Telephone: 818-506-8311 **Fax:** 818-506-8334
Website: www.jfala.com **E-Mail:** assistant@jfala.com
Departments and Staff:
    CEO - Jaime Ferrar;
    Commercial - Joey Robson
Ages Represented: 6+
Details: Children over the age of 6 and adults are represented in TV, film, and commercials. They are known for having a long list of bilingual Latin-American talent.
Tips: Submissions are accepted by mail or by email. Please do not drop anything off.
[SAG/AFTRA, AEA]

JKA TALENT AND LITERARY AGENCY

12725 Ventura Blvd., Suite H, Studio City, CA 91604
Telephone: 818-980-2093 **Website:** www.jkatalentagency.com
E-Mail: jkatalentagency@gmail.com

Departments and Staff:
President - James Kellem;
VP - Shannon McLaren;
Agent - Brad Benham
Details: This agency represents talent ages 2-64 for film, TV, comedy, and theatre. They also represent directors and writers.
Tips: Unsolicited submissions will not be accepted.
[DGA, WGA, ATA, SAG/AFTRA]

JORDAN MCKIRAHAN TALENT AGENCY (JMTA)

315 W Verdugo Avenue, #209, Burbank, CA 91502
Telephone: 818-955-8350   **Fax:** 818-955-8370
Website: www.jordanmckirahantalentagency.com
E-Mail: jordan@jm-ta.com
Ages Represented: All ages.
Details: Founded in 2009, this agency aims to honor its personal relationships with its clients while also supporting the progress of their business relationships.
Tips: Submit hardcopy materials (i.e. headshot, resume, and demo reel).
[SAG-AFTRA]

JS REPRESENTS

6815 Willoughby Avenue, #102, Los Angeles, CA 90038
Telephone: 323-462-3246   **Website:** www.jsrepresents.com
E-Mail: jsrepresents@mac.com
Departments and Staff:
Owner/Agent - Paul Jon Strotheide;
Agents - Lindy Gottlieb, Ann Kramer
Ages Represented: 18+
Details: Founded in 1990, this agency represents talent ages 18 and above for TV, commercials, and print.
Tips: Submissions are accepted by email only. Interviews are by appointment only.
[SAG/AFTRA]

KAZARIAN/MEASURES/RUSKIN & ASSOCIATES

11969 Ventura Boulevard, 3rd Floor, Box 7409,
Studio City, CA 91604
Telephone: 818-769-9111   **Fax:** 818-769-1824
Website: www.KMRtalent.com

NOTES

Departments and Staff:
Owner/CEO/Performers with Disabilities - Cindy Kazarian;
President - Mark Measures;
Partner/Sr. VP/On-Camera - Alicia Ruskin;
Equity Talent - Tal Fox;
On-Camera - Jamie Hernandez, Brooke Nuttall;
Theatrical - Tony Martinez, Michael Tzeiler, Harold Augenstein
Voiceover - Arlene Glucksman-Jones, Nathan Higgins;
Stunts and Sports - Heidi Hydar;
Performers with Disabilities - Gail Williamson;
Celebrity Endorsement - Fred Westbrook, Arlene Gluckman-Jones, Valerie Chiovetti;
Assistants - Sterling Davis, Andrew Morgan, Joe Ciccarone, Jacquie Adorni, Crystal Green, Mike Mason, Ryane Buttigieg, Gabriel Plante, Starr Hardin, Evan Mellinger, Abby Plante

Ages Represented: 5+

Details: This agency has offices in Los Angeles and New York. They represent talent for theatre, film, TV, stunts, voiceover, sports, and commercials.

Tips: Submissions are accepted by mail only. Unsolicited demos will not be accepted. Voice-over submissions accepted by email Interviews are by appointment only.

[ATA, NATR, SAG/AFTRA, AEA]

KEN LINDNER & ASSOCIATES

2029 Century Park East, #1000, Los Angeles, CA 90067
Telephone: 310-277-9223   **Fax:** 1-310-277-5806
Website: www.kenlindner.com
E-Mail: submissions@klateam.com

Departments and Staff:
CEO - Ken Lindner;
Co-President/Talent Representative - Karen Wang-Lavelle;
VPs - Melissa Van Fleet, Susan Levin;
Talent Representative - Rob Jordan;
Talent Development - Eric Moreno;
Director of Talent - Jill Walter;
Director of Operations - Tom Ragonnet;
Executive Assistant - Shari Freis

Details: KLA is known for representing talent for premier news and TV hosting, including hosts on coveted news programs or ancors and correspondents for major cable networks.

Tips: Submissions are accepted by mail or by email. Interviews are by appointment only. Look to the agency's website for specific requirements for demo tapes.

[SAG/AFTRA]

KOHNER, INC., PAUL

9300 Wilshire Boulevard, #555, Beverly Hills, CA 90212
Telephone: 310-550-1060   **Fax:** 310-276-1083
Website: kohneragency.com
Departments and Staff:
    President - Pearl Wexler;
    Agents - Samantha Crisp, Amanda Glazer, John Coffey;
    Literary Head - Stephen Moore
Details: The Kohner Agency was founded in the 1930's, making it the second oldest talent agency in Los Angeles. They represent talent for performance and writing in film, TV, and theatre.
Tips: This agency accepts industry referrals only. Unsolicited submissions will not be accepted.
[DGA, WGA, ATA, SAG/AFTRA, AEA]

L & L TALENT

4010 Palos Verdes Dr. North Suite 200-D, Rolling Hills, CA 90274
Fax: 310-606-2751   **Website:** www.lltalent.com
E-Mail: Info@lltalent.com
Departments and Staff:
    Owner/Partner/Agent - Melody Lomboy;
    Partner/Theatrical - Lara Holmes; Agent - Mandy Jezin
Details: This family owned agency was established in 2006, and aims to serve as an agency for actors by actors.
Tips: Submissions are accepted by email. No phone calls please. Their full submission policy can be found online.
[SAG/AFTRA, AEA]

LA TALENT/LA MODELS

7700 W. Sunset Boulevard, Los Angeles, CA 90046
Telephone: 323-436-7700   **Website:** www.lamodels.com
E-Mail: management@lamodels.com, info@latalent.com
Departments and Staff:
    Director, LA Talent - Jenine Leigh;
    Commercial Agents, LA Talent - Rick Ferrari, Kristin Malecki;
    Agents, LA Models - Mary Anderson, Christa Klayman, Anahid Krile;
    Print, LA Models - Pam Loar;
    Children's Department - Tracy Dwyer
Tips: Submissions are accepted by mail only. Interviews are by appointment only.
[ATA, SAG/AFTRA]

NOTES

LAYA GELFF TALENT & LIT AGENCY

16133 Ventura Boulevard, Suite 700, Encino, CA 91436
Telephone: 818-996-3100
Departments and Staff: President - Laya Gelff
Ages Represented: 18-64
Tips: Actors must be submitted by industry referral only.
[SAG/AFTRA, DGA, WGA, AEA]

LEAVITT AGENCY

11500 West Olympics Boulevard, Suite 400
Los Angeles, CA 90064
Telephone: 310-444-3066
E-Mail: leavittagency@msn.com
Departments and Staff:
    President - Jeffrey Leavitt
    Assistant - Bette Thienapirak
Ages Represented: 18+
Details: This agency works with established talent for theatre, film, and TV.
Tips: Actors must be submitted by industry referral only.
[SAG/AFTRA]

LEMON LIME AGENCY

3245 Casitas Avenue, Suite 107, Los Angeles, CA, 90039
Telephone: 323-662-5100
Website: www.lemonlimeagency.com
E-Mail: newfaces@lemonlimeagency.com
Departments and Staff:
    Co-Founders/Agents - Robin Harrington, Chaim Magnum;
    Agent - Muriel Rivera
Details: This agency has earned a reputation for representing off-beat performers. Its co-founders have described their business concept as "talent with a twist."
Tips: Submissions are accepted by email only. Material should be sent as a link, not as attachments.

THE LEVIN AGENCY

8484 Wilshire Boulevard, #750, Beverly Hills, CA 90211
Telephone: 323-653-7073   **Website:** www.levintalent.com
E-Mail: sid@thelevinagency.com
Departments and Staff:
    Owner/Agent - Sid Levin;
    Agent - Patricia Levin

Details: Established in 1985, this agency represents talent of all ages for theatre, film, TV, commercials, print, comedy, voiceover, and dance. The Levin Agency has earned a reputation for representing underdog talent for a competative world.
Tips: Submissions are accepted by email only. Interviews are by appointment. No calls or walk-ins.
[SAG/AFTRA]

LEWIS & BEAL TALENT AGENCY

15303 Ventura Boulevard, Suite 900, Sherman Oaks, CA 91403
Telephone: 818-380-3099   **Fax:** 818-380-3029
E-Mail: info@lbtalent.com
Departments and Staff:
   President - Jackie Lewis;
   Agents - Debbie Palmer-Beal, Katie Floyd, Galit Finkelstein
Details: Established in 2009, this agency represents talent for film, theatre, TV, commercials, and print.
[ATA]

LINDA MCALISTER TALENT

30 North Raymond Ave, Suite 213, Pasadena, CA 91103
Telephone: 626-529-5739   **Website:** www.lmtalent.com
E-Mail: linda@lmtalent.com
Departments and Staff:
   Owner/Agent - Linda McAlister;
   Assistants - Molly McAlister, Robin Read
Ages Represented: All ages.
Details: The Los Angeles branch of the agency represents theatrical actors for film and TV.
Tips: Submissions are accepted through the agency's website and email only. No drop-offs or walk-ins allowed.
SAG/AFTRA

LW1, INC.

9378 Wilshire Boulevard, #310, Beverly Hills, CA 90212
Telephone: 310-601-2532   **Website:** www.lw1agency.com
Departments and Staff:
   VP - Sean Robinson;
   Commercial - Mark Park
Ages Represented: 15+
Details: Established in 1990, this agency specializes in commercial talent.
Tips: Submissions are accepted by mail or by email. Interviews are by appointment only.
[SAG/AFTRA]

MADEMOISELLE TALENT AGENCY

3550 Wilshire Boulevard, Suite 1610, Los Angeles, CA 90010
Telephone: 213-387-9994 **E-Mail:** wonlee55@yahoo.com
Departments and Staff:
 Owner - Won Lee;
 Agent - Alan Siegel
Details: This agency represents talent of all ages for film, TV, theatre, print, comedy, commercial, voiceover, broadcast journalism, and dance.
Tips: Submissions are accepted by mail only. Interviews are by appointment only.
[SAG/AFTRA]

MAGDALENA TALENT

1600 Rosecrans Avenue, 4th Floor, Manhattan Beach, CA 90266
Telephone: 310-355-8501 **Website:** www.magdalenatalent.com
Details: Established in 2008, this agency represents talent for film and commercials.
[SAG/AFTRA]

MALIBU ARTISTS AGENCY

23732 Malibu Road, Santa Monica, CA 90265
Telephone: 310-985-9342 **Fax:** 424-644-0452
Website: www.malibuartistsagency.com
E-Mail: kim.malibuartistsagency@yahoo.com
Departments and Staff:
 Kim Cunningham
Details: MAA represents all ages for commercials and print.
Tips: The agency can be contacted via the email on the website. They are seeking for union and non-union talent.
[SAG/AFTRA]

MARLENE AGENCY, THE

6080 Center Drive, Suite 694, Los Angeles, CA 90045
Telephone: 310-578-5099 **Website:** www.themarleneagency.com
E-Mail: marnie28@ca.rr.com
Departments and Staff:
 Agent - Marlene Hartjeq
Details: This agency represents actors and performers of all types.
Tips: Inquiries can be made through Marlene's website.
[SAG/AFTRA]

MAVRICK ARTISTS AGENCY, INC.

8383 Wilshire Boulevard, Suite #330, Beverly Hills, CA 90211
Telephone: 323-931-5555 **Fax:** 323-931-5554
Website: www.mavrickartists.com
Departments and Staff:
Agents - Brad Diffley, Michael McConnell, Erick Negri, Christina Price, Larry Wiedmann, Penny Middlemiss, Samantha Daniels, Heather Martin, Stephanie Pabalinas, Ted Mair
Details: This agency represents talent of all ages for print, comedy, TV, modeling, voiceover, commercials, film, and sports personalities.
Tips: Submissions are by mail only. Interviews are by appointment only.
[ATA, SAG/AFTRA]

MCDONALD/SELZNICK ASSOCIATES

953 Cole Avenue, Hollywood, CA 90038
Telephone: 323-957-6680 **Fax:** 323-957-6688
Website: www.msaagency.com
Departments and Staff:
Partners - Julie McDonald, Tony Selznick;
Choreographers - Andrew Jacobs;
Dance/On-Camera - JC Gutierrez, Melissa Perez, Jenn Proctor;
Assistants - Carly Friedlander, Megan Hunt, Annie Pierce
Details: MSA has offices in Los Angeles and New York. They represent talent of all ages in theatre, film, TV, music, dance, and commercials. They also represent stage directors and body doubles.
Tips: Submit through the website. Submission requirements differ by department.
[ATA, SAG/AFTRA, AEA]

MCHUGO ARTISTS AGENCY

11350 Ventura Blvd., #208, Studio City, CA 91604
Telephone: 323-455-4811 **Website:** www.mchugoartists.com
E-Mail: info@mchugoartists.com
Ages Represented: 18+
Details: They represent adults in TV, film, and commercials.
Tips: Although the agency prefers industry referrals, submissions can be made on the form on their website.

[SAG/AFTRA]

NOTES

MEDIA ARTISTS GROUP

8222 Melrose Avenue, #203, Los Angeles, CA 90046
Telephone: 323-658-5050
Website: www.mediaartistsgroup.com
E-Mail: info@mediaartistsgroup.com
Departments and Staff:
    President/Theatrical - Raphael Berko;
    President/Literary - Barbara Alexander;
    Agents - Lynea Bell, Fred Coleman, Sheila Legette, Robin Nassif;
    Kids/Commercial - Francine Marseille;
    Commercial - Steven Erdek;
    Personal Appearances/Live Events - Mr. Ness;
    Agent/Assistant to Raphael - Ruby Martin
Details: MAG represents talent of all ages for film, TV, voiceover, and commercials. They also represent writers and producers.
Tips: Submissions are accepted by mail only. They prefer industry referrals. Interviews are by appointment only.
[DGA, WGA, SAG/AFTRA, AEA]

MZA "MICHAEL ZANUCK AGENCY"

28035 Dorothy Drive, #1120, Agoura Hills, CA 90010
Telephone: 818-707-9747 **Fax:** 818-707-9751
Website: www.michaelzanuckagency.com
E-Mail: michaelzanuck@gmail.com
Departments and Staff:
    Owner/CEO/Chief Theatrical Agent - Michael Zanuck;
Details: MZA "The Michael Zanuck Agency" represents talent in TV, film, commercials, print, and hosting. They represent all ages.
[ATA]

MITCHELL K. STUBBS & ASSOCIATES

8695 Washington Boulevard, Suite 204, Culver City, CA 90232
Telephone: 310-838-1200 **Fax:** 310-838-1245
Website: www.mksagency.com **E-Mail:** mks@mksagency.com
Departments and Staff:
    President/Owner - Mitchell K. Stubbs;
    VP - Judy Page; Commercials - Maria Walker

NOTES

Details: MKS works with actors of all ages, including teens and young adults, in film and TV.
Tips: Submissions can be made through industry referral only.
[SAG/AFTRA, AEA, WGA, DGA, ATA]

MOMENTUM TALENT AND LITERARY

9401 Wilshire Boulevard, #501, Beverly Hills, CA 90212
Telephone: 310-858-6655 **Website:** www.momentumtal.com
E-Mail: info@momentumtal.com
Departments and Staff:
    Owner/Agent - Garry Purdy;
    Theatrical - Mike Baldridge, Alicia Bravatti;
    Youth - Patti Townsend
Details: This agency represents talent of all ages in print, commericals, film, TV, and theatre.
Tips: Submissions are accepted by mail or through their website. Industry referrals are preferred. Interviews are by appointment only.
[ATA, SAG/AFTRA]

NANCY CHAIDEZ AGENCY & ASSOC.

6340 Coldwater Canyon Boulevard, #214
North Hollywood, CA 91606
Telephone: 323-467-8954 **Fax:** 323-467-8963
Website: www.nancychaidez.com
E-Mail: info@nancychaidez.com
Departments and Staff:
    Owner/Agent - Nancy Chaidez;
    Director of General Talent - Maria Chaidez
Details: This agency represents talent of all ages for print, comedy, broadcasting, modeling TV, film, stunts, sports personalities, voiceover, and dance. They also represent writers and producers.
Tips: Submissions are accepted by mail or email, but email is preferred. Interviews are by appointment only.
[WGA, SAG/AFTRA]

NETWORK INT'L MODELS AND TALENT

215 South La Cienega Boulevard, #205, Beverly Hills, CA 90211
Telephone: 310-855-0166 **Website:** www.network-models.com

Details: This agency has offices in Los Angeles, Scottsdale, and Tucson.
Tips: Refer to the agency's website for submission information.

NEXT MANAGEMENT

8447 Wilshire Boulevard, Penthouse, Beverly Hills, CA 90211
Telephone: 323-782-0010   **Fax:** 323-782-0035
Website: www.nextmanagement.com
E-Mail: submissions@nextmodels.com
Details: This agency has offices in Los Angeles, New York, Miami, Paris, London, and Milan. They represent talent for print and modeling. They also represent musicians, hair/makeup artists, and chefs.
Tips: Submissions are accepted online. Refer to website for specific instructions.

NOBLE ARTISTS
@RALEIGH STUDIOS

1000 Universal City Plaza, Universal City, CA, 91608
Telephone: 310-956-7501   **Toll Free:** 855-385-6428
Website: dcosgro.wix.com/noble-artists
E-Mail: info@nobletaelnt.tv (no hard submissions, please)
Departments and Staff:
　　CEO/Manager - Doug Cosgro;
　　Theatrical/TV - Jodi Mankewitz;
　　Commercials - Clarke Renfro;
　　Literary - Tyler Madden;
　　Model/Print - Leland Haskins;
　　Latin Market - Javier Espranza;
　　Comedy - Patrick Murphy;
　　Children - Lisa Borsema;
　　New Orleans Office - Mame Beaudry;
　　Las Vegas Office - Richard Blakey
Ages Represented: All ages.
Details: Represents actors, models, comedians, and musicians for film, TV, commercials, and print. This agency specializes in the representation of theatrical and comedic-actors, writers, children, live-performers, and web-new media. They also have locations in Las Vegas, San Francisco and New Orleans.
Tips: No hard copy submissions, email is preferred. Industry referrals preferred but not required. Interviews are by appointment only.
[SAG/AFTRA]

NORWOOD TALENT AGENCY CORPORATION

6355 Topanga Canyon Boulevard, #520
Woodland Hills, CA 91367
Telephone: 818-716-1115 **Fax:** 818-716-1144
E-Mail: info@ntacla.com
Departments and Staff:
    President/Agent - Sonja Norwood;
    Agents - Rayva Harrell, Willie Norwood
Details: NTAC represents young talent for film, TV, voiceover, and commercials.
Tips: Submissions are accepted online only.
[SAG/AFTRA]

NTA

1445 N Stanley Avenue, 2nd Floor, Los Angeles, CA 90046
Telephone: 323-969-0113 **Website:** www.ntatalent.com
E-Mail: nta@ntatalent.com
Departments and Staff:
    President/Owner - Nick Terzian;
    Commercial - Eddie Winkler; Hosting/Print - Kati Herrera;
    Print - James Delio; Assistants - Rachel Herrick, Tiara
    Tervel
Details: NTA represents talent of all ages for print, comedy, modeling, stunts, film, TV, sports personalities, and dance. They also represent magicians.
Tips: Submissions are accepted by mail or by email. No phonecalls or drop-offs are accepted.
[SAG/AFTRA]

NU TALENT AGENCY

117 N Robertson Boulevard, #A, Los Angeles, CA 90048
Telephone: 310-385-6900 **Fax:** 310-385-6910
Website: nutalentagency.com **E-Mail:** info@nutalentagency.com
Departments and Staff:
    Agent - Anna Rossi; Agent - Allie Faythe;
    Director of Commercials - Alex Fox
Ages Represented: All ages.
Details: This agency represents actors, models and children for commercials and endorsements.
Tips: Please email materials to info@nutalentagency.com. No calls.
[SAG/AFTRA]

NOTES

O'NEILL TALENT GROUP

4150 Riverside Drive, Burbank, CA 91505
Telephone: 818-566-7717 **Fax:** 818-566-7725
Website: www.oneilltalent.com **E-Mail:** oneilltalent@gmail.com
Departments and Staff:
   Agent - Sheila Ellis;
   Assistants - Eva Barrial, Kristen Johnson
Details: This agency represents talent for commercials, film, TV, and theatre. They specialize in improvisation and sketch comedians.
Tips: Only industry referrals are considered for submissions. Unsolicited headshots will not be accepted. Interviews are by appointment only.
[SAG/AFTRA]

ORIGIN TALENT AGENCY

4705 Laurel Canyon Boulevard, #306, Valley Village, CA 91607
Telephone: 818-487-1800 **Fax:** 818-487-1849
Departments and Staff:
   Owner/Theatrical & Commercial - Annie Schwartz;
   Owner/Theatrical - Marc Chancer;
   Associate Agent - Tim O'Shae
Details: This agency represents talent of all ages for film, TV, comedy, and commercials.
Tips: Submissions are accepted by mail or by email, but email is preferred. Interviews are by appointment only.
[SAG/AFTRA]

OSBRINK TALENT AGENCY

4343 Lankershim Boulevard #100, Universal City, CA 91602
Telephone: 818-760-2488 **Fax:** 818 760 0991
Website: www.osbrinkagency.com
E-Mail: contact@osbrinkagency.com
Departments and Staff:
   Head of Theatrical/Partner - Cindy Osbrink;
   Head of Commercial, Print, & Publicity/Partner - Scott Wine;
   VP of Youth Theatrical/Agent - Emily Urbani;
   Theatrical/Junior Agent - Yasmine Pearl;
   Theatrical/Assistant - Samantha Gordon;
   Youth Theatrical/Assistant - Nicole Milakovich;
   VP of Operations - Angela Strange;
   Adult Commercial & Print/Assistant - Lindsay Cooley;
   VP of Youth Commercial & Print/Agent - Dawn Osbrink;

Youth Commercial & Contract Administrator/Agent - Aysha Brown;
Youth Commercial & Print/Assistant - Murjani Gaither;
Head Of Youth & Adult Voiceover/Agent - Maureen Rose;
Youth & Adult Voiceover/Agent - Robert Saulog;
Youth & Adult Voiceover/Assistant - Brooke Kolisar

Details: This agency represents talent of all ages for film, TV, commercials, voiceover, and print.

Tips: Submissions are accepted by mail or through their website. Interviews are by appointment only.

[ATA, SAG/AFTRA]

PACIFIC TALENT & MODELS, INC.

1600 Rosecrans Media Center, 4th Floor,
Manhattan Beach, CA 90266
Telephone: 310-321-7670
Website: www.pacifictalentandmodels.com
E-Mail: info@pacifictalent.tv
Details: This agency represents talent in TV, film, print, modeling, and commercials.
Tips: Submissions are accepted by email or should be mailed to the following address: 1600 Rosecrans Ave Media Center, 4th Fl Manhattan Beach, CA 90266 and should include "ATTN: New Faces.

PAKULA/KING & ASSOCIATES

9229 W Sunset Boulevard, Suite 400, West Hollywood, CA 90069
Telephone: 310-281-4868   **Fax:** 310-281-4866
Departments and Staff:
    Owner - Joel King;
    Agents - Gabe Watkins, Ben Gorman
Ages Represented: 18+
Details: The majority of their clients are adults but they do represent children. They specialize in TV and film.
Tips: Submissions need an industry referral, and walk-ins are not allowed.
[SAG/AFTRA, AEA]

PANTHEON

1801 Century Park East, Suite #1910, Los Angeles, CA 90067
Telephone: 310-201-0120   **Fax:** 310-201-5958
Website: pantheontalent.com
E-Mail: rice@pantheontalent.com

NOTES

Departments and Staff:
President/Agent - Stephen Rice;
Partner/Literary - Susan Sussman-Laaks;
Theatrical - Cole Harris, Mike Wilson;
Commercial - Patricia Dawson, Pierre Gatling;
Literary - Rachel LeGault, Susan Sussman;
Print - Christi Carballo, Tag Turner
Details: This agency represents talent of all ages for print, comedy, TV, film, theatre, modeling, sports personalities, and commercials. They also represent musicians, production designers, directors, and film editors.
Tips: This agency accepts referrals only.
[DGA, WGA, ATA, SAG/AFTRA, AEA]

PARADIGM

360 N Crescent Drive, Beverly Hills, CA 90210
Telephone: 310-288-8000 **Fax:** 310-288-2000
Website: www.paradigmagency.com
Departments and Staff:
Chairman - Sam Gores;
CFO - Todd Quinn; VPs - Lawrence Antoine, Craig Wagner
Details: This is a top ten agency. Founded in 1992, this agency has offices in Beverly Hills, Monterey, Nashville, and New York. They represent talent for film, TV, theatre, print, voiceover, commercials, and dance. They also represent writers, cinematographers, directors, production designers, and film editors.
Tips: Submissions are accepted by mail only. Unsolicited demos will not be accepted.
[DGA, WGA, SAG/AFTRA, AEA]

PARTOS COMPANY

227 Broadway, #204, Santa Monica, CA 90401
Telephone: 310-458-7800 **Website:** www.partos.com
E-Mail: partos@partos.com
Departments and Staff:
Owner/Agent - Walter Partos;
Film/TV - Alex Franklin;
Commercial/Music Videos - Martijn Hostetler
Details: This agency represents talent for film, TV, and commercials. They also represent cinematographers, production designers, and costume/makeup designers. They have offices in Los Angeles, New York, and Canada.
[DGA, SAG/AFTRA]

PINNACLE COMMERCIAL TALENT

5055 Wilshire Boulevard, #865, Los Angeles, CA 90036
Telephone: 323-939-5440 **Fax:** 323-939-0630
Departments and Staff:
    Owners - John Frazier, Mike Eisenstadt;
    Partner - Gloria Hinojosa;
    Commercial - Joan Messinger
Details: This agency specializes in commercial talent.
Tips: Submissions are accepted by mail and fax only. Interviews are by appointment.
[ATA, SAG/AFTRA]

PLAYERS TALENT AGENCY, INC.

16130 Ventura Boulevard, #235, Encino, CA 91436
Telephone: 818-990-9577 **E-Mail:** playerstnt@yahoo.com
Departments and Staff:
    Owner/Agent - Joe Kolkowitz
Details: This agency represents talent for comedy, broadcasting, film, TV, sports personalities, and commercials.
Tips: Drop-offs will not be accepted.
[SAG/AFTRA]

PREMIER TALENT GROUP, THE

4370 Tujunga Avenue, #110, Studio City, CA 91604
Telephone: 818-752-5911 **Fax:** 866-469-0944
Website: www.thepremiertalentgroup.com
E-Mail: info@thepremiertalentgroup.com
Departments and Staff:
    Owner/Head of Theatrical Division - James J. Jones;
    Agent - Erika Godwin
Details: This agency books talent for film, TV, and commercials.
Tips: Headshots, resumes, and demos can be submitted by mail or email. All application materials will be shredded after review.
[SAG/AFTRA]

PRIVILEGE TALENT AGENCY

17514 Ventura Boulevard, #105, Encino, CA 90028
Telephone: 818-386-2377 **E-Mail:** privilegetalent@yahoo.com
Departments and Staff:
    Owner/Agent - Carol Oleesky;
    Print - Melanie Allen

NOTES

Details: This agency represents talent for print, comedy, broadcasting, modeling, stunts, sports personalities, film, TV, and dance.
Tips: Submissions are accepted by mail only. Interviews are by appointment only.
[SAG/AFTRA]

PRODIGY TALENT AGENCY

7080 Hollywood Boulevard, #1100, Los Angeles, CA 90028
Telephone: 310-462-2310   **Website:** www.prodigytalent.net
E-Mail: submissions@prodigytalent.net
Departments and Staff:
   Agents - Audrey Pierz, Bazel Gold
Details: They handle acting talent for commercials, film, and TV.
Tips: Submissions are accepted via email only. Make sure that headshot and resume files are embedded into the body of the email. Multilingual applicants and those with improvisation training are encouraged to apply.
SAG/AFTRA, NON-UNION

PROGRESSIVE ARTISTS

9696 Culver Boulevard, Suite 110, Culver City , CA 90232
Telephone: 310-559-9700
E-Mail: progressiveartists@gmail.com
Departments and Staff:
   Agents - Bernard Carneol,
   Belle Zwerdling, Jillana Devine
Tips: Submissions are accepted by mail only. Interviews are by appointment only.
[ATA, SAG/AFTRA, AEA]

Q MODELS TALENT MANAGEMENT

8618 West 3rd Street, Los Angeles, CA 90048
Telephone: 310-205-2888   **Website:** www.qmodels.com
E-Mail: la@qmanagementinc.com
Departments and Staff:
   Owner - Jeffrey Kolsrud;
   Print/Commercial - Shelly Kolsrud;
   Print - Cynthia Cheng, Chris Saavedra
Details: Founded in 1998, this agency has offices in New York and Los Angeles. They represent talent for print, modeling, film, and TV.
Tips: Submssions are accepted by email or by their open call.
[SAG/AFTRA]

QUALITA DELL'ARTE

5353 Topanga Canyon Boulevard, Woodland Hills, CA, 91364
Telephone: 818-598-8073
Details: This agency represents actors and writers.

RAGE MODELS & TALENT AGENCY

23679 Calabasas Road, #501, Calabasas, CA 91302
Telephone: 818-225-0526   **Fax:** 818-225-1736
Website: www.ragemodels.com   **E-Mail:** info@ragemodels.com
Departments and Staff:
    President/Agent - Elaine Parker;
    Fit & Print Agent - Faith Lorenzen;
    Talent Agent - Joann Smolen;
    Assistant - Adrienne DiLuigi
Details: Established in 1993, this agency represents talent for print, modeling, commercials, film, and TV.
Tips: Submissions are accepted by mail or throught their website.
[ATA, SAG/AFTRA]

RASCALS TALENT AGENCY

2219 W. Olive Ave #273, Burbank CA 90506
Telephone: 323-686-6001   **Website:** www.rascalstalent.com
E-Mail: rascalstalent@aol.com
Details: Submissions are only accepted through email at rascaltalent@aol.com.

REBEL ENTERTAINMENT PARTNERS

5700 Wilshire Boulevard, #456, Los Angeles, CA 90036
Telephone: 323-935-1700   **Website:** www.reptalent.com
E-Mail: inquiry@reptalent.com
Departments and Staff:
    President - Richard Lawrence;
    Executive Vice President - Debra Goldfarb;
    CFO - Joyce Goertzen; Senior Vice President - Philip Irven;
    Vice President, Theatrical Division - Matt Jackson;
    Agents - Denise Prayer, Jared Thompson, Alexandra
    Bourbon
Details: Represents talent for reality TV, news, game shows as well as selectively representing theatrical clients.
Tips: Industry referral only. No unsolicited submissions.
[DGA, WGA, ATA, SAG/AFTRA]

NOTES

REGWAN TALENT AGENCY

1875 Century Park East, #700, Los Angeles, CA 90067
Telephone: 310-284-6858

REIGN AGENCY

400 S Beverly Dr., Suite 250, Beverly Hills, CA 90212
Telephone: 310-396-6462   **Fax:** 310-396-6415
Website: www.reignagency.com
E-Mail: laura@reignagency.com
Departments and Staff:
    President - Laura Soo Hoo;
    Youth Agent - Lindsay Mass;
    Theatrical Agent - Megan Rice
Details: Represents infants as well as adults in film, TV and commercials.
Tips: Industry referral only; No unsolicited submissions
[ATA, SAG/AFTRA]

RPM TALENT GROUP/ THE AGENCY

2600 West Olive Avenue, 5th Floor, Burbank, CA 91505
Telephone: 818-333-5150   **Website:** www.rpmtalent.com
E-Mail: info@rpmtalent.com
Departments and Staff:
    CEO/Agent - Tiffany Atwood,
    Extreme Division - Shawn Barry
    High Fashion Print - Jo Kimberly;
    PR - Jennifer Sims
Ages Represented: All Ages.
Details: Represents actors, print models, music artists, dancers, and sports personalities. They work with all ages in theatrical and commercial.
Tips: Submissions are accepted by email or mail. Interviews by appointment only.
[SAG/AFTRA/WGA]

S D B PARTNERS, INC.

315 S Beverly Dr, Suite 411., Beverly Hills, CA 90212
Telephone: 310-785-0060
Departments and Staff:
    Partners - Louis Bershad, Ro Diamond, Susie Schwarz;
    Agent - Steven Jang
Details: Represents actors in film, TV and theater. No children.
Tips: Industry referral only; no unsolicited submissions.
[SAG/AFTRA, AEA]

SASCO HILL & ASSOCIATES

4340 Lyceum Avenue, Los Angeles, CA, 90066
Telephone: 310-966-0797 **Fax:** 310-362-0420
E-Mail: sascohill@att.net
Departments and Staff: Agents - Amanda Fouraker, Judy
   Scheffel, Jason Vaughn

SAVAGE AGENCY, THE

6212 Banner Avenue, Hollywood, CA 90038
Telephone: 323-461-8316 **Website:** savageagency.net
E-Mail: info@thesavageagency.net
Departments and Staff:
   President/Owner - Judy Savage;
   Agents - Jennifer Boyce, Stella Alex, Jason Barias,
   Mark Smith,
Details: Please do not call. Send submissions by mail.
Tips: They represent children, teens, young adults, and adults
working in TV, film, and commercials.
[SAG/AFTRA, AEA]

SCHIOWITZ/CONNOR/
ANKRUM/WOLF

1680 N Vine Street, #1016, Los Angeles, CA 90028
Telephone: 323-463-8355 **Fax:** 323-463-7355
Departments and Staff:
   Partners/Agents - David Ankrum, Erin Connor;
   Agents - Caleigh Vancata, Steve Walker, Steven Dry,
   Stephanie Hoover
Ages Represented: 18+
Details: This agency represents actors and writers for theatre,
film, and TV.
Tips: Headshots and resumes can be submitted by mail only.
Interviews will be held by appointment only.
[WGA, SAG/AFTRA, AEA]

SCREEN ARTISTS AGENCY

16505 Arminta St., Van Nuys, CA 91406
Telephone: 818-487-8880 **Fax:** 818-487-8883
Website: www.screenartistsagency.com
E-Mail: submission@screenartistsagency.com
Departments and Staff:
   Owner/Agent - Cyndee Burditt;
   Agent - Erica Hunton

Details: They represent talent of all ages for commercials, film, and TV.
Tips: Submit headshots and resumes by mail only. Interviews will be held by appointment only.
[SAG/AFTRA]

SELLMAN GROUP

14145 Albers Street, Sherman Oaks, CA 91401
Telephone: 818-786-8424
E-Mail: thesellmangroup@hotmail.com
Tips: Submit headshots and resumes by mail only. Interviews will be held by appointment only.

SHIRLEY WILSON AND ASSOCIATES

14140 Ventura Boulevard #206, Sherman Oaks, CA, 91423
Telephone: 323-857-6977
E-Mail: wilsontalentagency@gmail.com
Departments and Staff:
    Owner/Agent - Greg Culver
[SAG/AFTRA, WGA]

SIONA ENTERTAINMENT

3619 W Magnolia Boulevard, #450, Burbank, CA 91505
Telephone: 310-634-5050
Website: www.sionaentertainment.com
E-Mail: agent@sionaentertainment.com
Ages Represented: All ages.
Details: They represents both actors and models. They book talent for print, commercials, voiceovers, film, TV, theatre, and fashion.
Tips: This agency prefers to accept submissions via mail or email. However, drop-offs will also be looked at.

SMITH & HERVEY/GRIMES TALENT AGENCY

3002 Midvale Avenue Suite 206, Los Angeles, CA 90034
Telephone: 310-475-2010 **Website:** www.herveygrimes.com
E-Mail: assistant@herveygrimes.com
Departments and Staff:
    Agents - Pam Grimes, Marsha Hervey, Julie Smith;
    Associate - Natalie Kollar

Details: This agency represents children and older for print, comedy, voiceover, film, and TV.
Tips: Submissions are accepted by mail or by email. Interviews by appointment only.
[SAG/AFTRA]

SMS TALENT

8383 Wilshire Boulevard, Suite 230, Beverly Hills, CA 90211
Telephone: 310-289-0909 **Fax:** 310-289-0990
Website: www.smstalent.com
Departments and Staff:
    Owner - Donna Massetti;
    Partners - Gregg Mehlman, Charles Silver, Ian Roumain;
    Assistant - Ally Matteo
Ages Represented: 18+
Details: SMS Talent represents actors for theatre, film, and TV.
Tips: This agency accepts industry referrals only.
[ATA, SAG/AFTRA, AEA]

SOLID TALENT AGENCY

2919 W Burbank Boulevard, Burbank, CA 91505
Telephone: 818-845-0808 **Fax:** 818-845-8812
Website: www.solidtalent.com
E-Mail: mikesoliday@solidtalent.com
Departments and Staff:
    Owner/Agent - Mike Soliday;
    Voiceover - Micaela Stepanovich
Details: They book solely for voiceover work.
Tips: Send reels and demos by email only. Interviews are conducted by appointment only.
[SAG/AFTRA]

SOVEREIGN TALENT GROUP

1642 Westwood Boulevard, Suite 202, Los Angeles, CA 90024
Telephone: 310-474-4000 **Fax:** 310-474-4431
E-Mail: info@sovereigntg.com
Departments and Staff:
    President/Agent - Peter Young;
    Theatrical - Regan Froby, Eric Kind, Thomas Cook;
    Commercial - Nathan Habben, Susan Havins;
    Print - Anthony Fernandez

NOTES

Details: This agency represents a variety of talent of all ages for film, TV, theatre, commercials, voiceovers, print, and specialty.
Tips: To apply, mail or email submission materials. Interviews are granted by appointment only.
[SAG/AFTRA]

SPECIAL ARTISTS AGENCY

9200 West Sunset Boulevard, #410, West Hollywood, CA 90069
Telephone: 310-859-9688 **Website:** www.specialartists.com
E-Mail: reception@specialartists.com
Departments and Staff: President - Elizabeth Dalling
Details: They handle talent for voiceover and commercial work.
Tips: This agency only accepts industry referrals.
[SAG/AFTRA]

SPORTS + LIFESTYLE UNLIMITED

8265 W Sunset Boulevard, Suite. 203, West Hollywood, CA 90046
Telephone: 323-654-6555 **Fax:** 323-421-9347
Website: www.sluagency.com
Departments and Staff:
　　President - Dave Weiss;
　　Executive Vice President - Paul Herschell;
　　Director of Booking - Karen Osborn;
　　Booking Assistant - Emily Petkus; On-Camera - Michael Huth;
　　Print - Geraldine Marquez; Talent - Alison Lo
Details: They represent talent of all ages for film, TV, commercials, print, and specialty. Their Portland office is home to owners, Dave and Paul, as well as Molly Weiss, director of booking. Karen Osborn heads the LA office.
Tips: Interested parties should apply via the website's online submission form only. No walk-ins.

STAGE 9/DDO

4605 Lankershim Boulevard #340, North Hollywood, CA 91602
Telephone: 323-462-8000 **Website:** www.stage9talent.com
E-Mail: stage9@ddoagency.com
Departments and Staff:
　　Agents - Jaime Jerugim, Carol Weiss, Blossom Wagner
Details: Their departments include a teens and children division, as well as representation in TV, film, theatre, and commercials.
Tips: Submissions are only accepted through US mail.
[SAG/AFTRA]

THE STANDER GROUP, INC.

4533 Van Nuys Boulevard, # 401, Sherman Oaks, CA 91403
Telephone: 818-905-7000 **Fax:** 818-905-6813
Website: www.scottstander.com
E-Mail: submissions@scottstander.com
Departments and Staff:
   Agent - Jackie Stander;
   Agent - Scott Stander; Agent - Samantha Stander
Ages Represented: 5-80
Details: They work with children, teens and adults in TV, film, commercials, theatre, concerts, and personal appearances.
Tips: Submissions can be made by mail only. No drop-offs or emails accepted.
[SAG/AFTRA, AEA]

STARCRAFT TALENT AGENCY

27525 Newhall Ranch Road, Suite 7-D, 2nd Floor
Valencia, CA 91355
Telephone: 818-403-1105 **Website:** www.starcrafttalent.com
E-Mail: starcraftagency@gmail.com
Departments and Staff:
   Agent - Paula McAfee
Details: Represents talent above the age of 4 to adults. Talent above the age of 12 must be Union. They represent actors, comedians, and stuntpeople in TV, film, print, and commercials.
Tips: Submissions only accepted by mail and union actors are preferred. Do not drop off or call.
[SAG/AFTRA]

STONE MANNERS SALNERS

6100 Wilshire Blvd., Suite 1500, Los Angeles, CA 90048
Telephone: 323-655-1313 **Fax:** 323-389-1577
Website: www.smsagency.com **E-Mail:** info@smsagency.com
Departments and Staff:
   Partners/Agents - Tim Stone,
   Scott Manners, Glenn Salners;
   Associates - Samantha Huff, Michael Place;
   Coordinator, Hosting and Voiceover - Thomas Prochnow;
   Agents - Nicole Cataldo, Adrian Pellereau, Benjamin Sands
Details: This talent firm books actors and variety artists for voiceovers, commercials, theatre, film, and TV. They also have a location in New York.

Tips: Submit headshots and resumes by mail only. The agency accepts postcards and invitations. Interviews will be conducted by appointment only.
[SAG/AFTRA, AEA, ATA, DGA]

STUDIO TALENT GROUP

1328 12th Street, Santa Monica, CA 90401
Telephone: 310-393-8004   **Fax:** 310-872-5400
Website: www.studiotalentgroup.com
E-Mail: stgactor@gmail.com
Departments and Staff:
 Owner/Manager - Phil Brock;
 Vice President - Kathryn W. Boole;
 Talent - Travis Engle, Wendy Lungaro
Ages Represented: All ages.
Details: This agency represents actors for film, TV, theatre, and commercials. They also have a packaging as well as a literary department.
Tips: Submissions accepted by both mail and email. Postcards and invitations are welcomed.

SUSAN NATHE & ASSOC. (CPC)

8281 Melrose, #200, Los Angeles, CA 90046
Telephone: 323-653-7573   **Fax:** 323 653 1179
E-Mail: susan@susannathe.com
Departments and Staff:
 Principal - Susan Nathe
Details: This agency represents talent of all ages for print, TV, film, and commercials.
Tips: Submissions are accepted by mail only. Interviews are by appointment only.
[SAG/AFTRA, ATA]

SUTTON, BARTH & VENNARI, INC.

5900 Wilshire Boulevard, Suite 700, Los Angeles, CA 90036
Telephone: 323-938-6000   **Fax:** 323-935-8671
Website: www.sbvtalent.com   **E-Mail:** info@sbvtalent.com
Departments and Staff:
 President/Agent - Rita Vennari;
 Voiceover - Robin Lamel Adler, Mary Ellen Lord, Cynthia McLean, Jessica Bulavsky
 On-Camera - Pam Sparks, Rachele Fink
Details: They book actors for voiceovers and commercials.

Tips: Submissions can be sent by mail. Interviews will be held by appointment only.
[ATA, SAG/AFTRA]

SYNERGY TALENT

13251 Ventura Boulevard, #2, Studio City, CA 91604
Telephone: 818-995-6500
E-Mail: submissions@synergytalent.net
Departments and Staff:
 Owner/Theatrical Division - Karl Hofheinz;
 Voiceover - Jen Kamstock; Commercial - Kris Murrell-
 Diedrich
Ages Represented: 18+
Details: This agency books for film, TV, commercials, and voiceovers.
Tips: Commercial and voiceover submissions can be sent by email. They do not accept unsolicited theatrical submissions during pilot season. Interviews will be held by appointment only.

TALENT HOUSE LA

3000 Olympic Boulevard, #2350, Santa Monica, CA 90404
Telephone: 310-315-4797 **Fax:** 310-868-0204
Website: www.thetalenthousela.com
E-Mail: info@thetalenthousela.com
Departments and Staff:
 President - Tracy Curtis;
 Theatrical - Matt Gogal
Details: They book talent for film, TV, and commercial work.
Tips: This agency is looking for experienced talent of both union and non-union status. Submit all application materials via email to thetalenthousela2012@gmail.com.
[SAG/AFTRA]

TALENTWORKS

3500 W Olive Avenue, Suite 1400, Burbank, CA 91505
Telephone: 818-972-4300 **Fax:** 818-955-6411
Website: www.talentworks.us
Departments and Staff:
 Agents - Harry Gold, Brandy Gold, Suzanne Wohl, Marion
 Camble, August Kammer
Details: Started in 1982 by Harry Gold, TalentWorks represents children and adults in TV, film, and commercials.
Tips: Mail submissions only are accepted, as well as postcards and invitations. Industry referrals only.
[SAG/AFTRA, AEA, ATA,WGA,DGA]

NOTES

TGMD TALENT AGENCY

6767 Forest Lawn Drive, Suite #206, Los Angeles, CA 90068
Telephone: 323-850-6767 **Fax:** 323-850-7340
Website: www.tgmdtalent.com **E-Mail:** vanessa@tgmdtalent.com
Departments and Staff:
President - Vanessa Gilbert;
Partners - Ilko Drozdoski, Kevin Motley;
On-Camera Agent - Sally Kadison;
Talent Coordinator - Jazmin Rangel
Ages Represented: 18+
Details: They book for voiceover and commercial work.
Tips: This agency accepts submissions via email. Interviews are by appointment only. No drop-offs or walk-ins.
[SAG/AFTRA]

TILMAR TALENT AGENCY

6404 Wilshire Boulevard, #735, Los Angeles, CA 90048
Telephone: 310-623-9231 **Fax:** 310-623-9233
Website: www.tilmartalent.com **E-Mail:** submit@tilmartalent.com
Departments and Staff:
Agent - Elton Bolden
Details: This agency books actors and models for print, commercials, film, and TV.
Tips: Submit materials via mail or email. Interviews will be held by appointment only.

TRIO TALENT AGENCY

1502 Gardner Street, Los Angeles, CA 90046
Telephone: 323-851-6886 **Fax:** 323-851-6882
Website: www.triotalentagency.com,
E-Mail: triotalentagency@gmail.com
Departments and Staff:
Owner/Director of Dance, Choreography, and Print - Rodney Chester
Details: This agency represents talent for dance, choreography, print, and commercial. They book work for music videos, industrials, live performances, and tours.
Tips: Applicants can submit materials by mail or email. Do not send originals. Interviews will be granted by appointment only.
[SAG/AFTRA]

UNITED TALENT AGENCY

9336 Civic Center Drive, Beverly Hills, CA 90210
Telephone: 310-273-6700   **Fax:** 310-247-1111
Website: www.unitedtalent.com   **E-Mail:** info@unitedtalent.com
Departments and Staff:
  CEO - Jeremy Zimmer;
  Chairman, Board of Directors - James Berkus;
  Board of Directors - Peter Benedek, David Kramer, Tracey
  Jacobs, Jay Sures
Details: This is a top five agency. UTA represents performance, creative, and technical talent in the print, voiceover, film, TV, and theatre disciplines. They have a large production office that represents producers, directors of photography, production designers, costume designers, editors, visual effects supervisors, first assistant directors, second unit directors and stunt coordinators. They are also located in New York.
Tips: This agency accepts industry referrals only.
[SAG/AFTRA, AEA, DGA, WGA]

VALMAUR TALENT AGENCY

6671 Sunset Boulevard, Building 1585, #108,
Hollywood, CA 90028
Telephone: 818-308-5711   **Fax:** 206-333-0180
Website: www.valentspring.wix.com/valmaur
E-Mail: valmaur.talent@gmail.com
Departments and Staff:
  Owner - Valentina Graham;
  Agent - Virginia Arlene
Details: This agency books actors for commercial, film, and TV work.

VESTA TALENT

2537 Pacific Coast Highway, #108, Torrance, CA 90505
Telephone: 310-538-8298   **Website:** www.vestatalent.com
E-Mail: info@vestatalent.com
Departments and Staff:
  Agent - Jane Schulman
Details: This agency is located at Raleigh Studios in Manhattan Beach, CA but they recieve mail to the address listed above.
Tips: No phone calls allowed.
[SAG/AFTRA, ATA]

NOTES

VISION TALENT/MODELS

5870 West Jefferson, Studio L, Los Angeles, CA 90016
Telephone: 310-733-4440 **Fax:** 310-733-4441
Website: www.visionlosangeles.com
E-Mail: models@visionlosangeles.com
Departments and Staff:
President - Francine Champagne;
Women's - Meg Day, Rhiannon Webb;
Men's - Marco Servetti, Rhiannon Webb;
Commercial - Pamela Lyles, Martin Uy
Ages Represented: Female - 14-22, Male - 18-25
Details: They book young talent for print and commercials.
Tips: If interested, visit an open call on Tuesday or Thursday afternoons or email submission materials. Interviews are held by appointment only.
[ATA, SAG/AFTRA]

VOX, INC.

6420 Wilshire Boulevard, #1080, Los Angeles, CA 90048
Telephone: 323-655-8699 **Fax:** 323-852-1472
Website: www.voxusa.net
Departments and Staff: Owner/Agent - Wes Stevens;
Agents - Jeff Jones, Tom Lawless;
Audio - Jason Merrell
Details: This firm represents talent for voiceovers and unscripted TV.
Tips: This agency accepts industry referrals only.
[ATA, SAG/AFTRA]

WILLIAM KERWIN AGENCY

1605 North Cahuenga, #202, Hollywood, CA 90028
Telephone: 323-469-5155 **Fax:** 310-652-3645
Website: www.williamkerwinagency.com
E-Mail: wka@williamkerwinagency.com
Departments and Staff:
Agents - William Kerwin, Al Woods, Izzy Lewis, Christine Regwan, Rose Frohlich, Tina Hunt
Details: They only accept hard copies of mailed submissions.
Tips: They work with adults between the age of 25 to mid-30s and are open to new talent. They also have a literary department.
[SAG/AFTRA, ATA, WGA, AEA]

WILLIAM MORRIS ENDEAVOR ENT.

9601 Wilshire Boulevard, Floor 3, Beverly Hills, CA 90210
Telephone: 310-285-9000 **Fax:** 310-245-9010
Website: www.wmeentertainment.com
Departments and Staff:
    Co-CEOs - Ari Emanuel, Patrick Whitesell;
    Executive Vice President - Jennifer Walsh;
    Partners - Philip d'Amecourt, Warren Zavala, David
    Wirtschafter, Tom Wellington, Richard Weitz, Brad Slater,
    Stacy Mark, Sean Perry;
    Comedy - Drew Welborn; Theatrical - Phillip Sun;
    TV - Rick Rosen
Details: This is a top five agency. They represent talent for film, TV, commercials, print, and specialty. They are a top-of-the-line agency with locations on both coasts as well as Nashville, TN.
Tips: They do not accept submissions. Industry referrals only.
[SAG/AFTRA, ATA]

WILLIAMS TALENT AGENCY

111 North La Cienega Boulevard, Suite 8, Beverly Hills, CA 90211
Telephone: 310-424-8802 **Fax:** 310-674-7178
E-Mail: lw@wtaagency.com
Departments and Staff: Owner/Talent Agent - Larry O. Williams
    Jr.;
    Assistant - Marie Jenious

WORLD CLASS SPORTS

5777 West Century Boulevard, Suite #1070,
Los Angeles, CA 90045
Telephone: 310-665-9400 **Fax:** 310-665-9844
Website: www.worldclass-sports.com
E-Mail: wcsagent@pacbell.net
Departments and Staff: President/Agent - Don Franken;
    Vice President - Andy Woolf
Ages Represented: 18+
Details: This agency represents sports personalities for commercials, broadcast, and specialty. They work with athletes only with Division 1-A, professional or national level, for commercial and print only. They represent sports celebrities for endorsements and appearances.
Tips: Headshots and resumes can be sent via mail. No phone calls are allowed. Interviews are conducted by appointment only.
[SAG/AFTRA]

NOTES

XPOSE ENTERTAINMENT, INC.

1055 East Colorado Boulevard, #5, Pasadena, CA 91106
Telephone: 626-240-4674 **Fax:** 626-240-4699
Website: www.xposeinc.com **E-Mail:** contact@xposeinc.com
Departments and Staff: Agent - Norman Hopson
Details: They book talent for film, TV, theatre, print, commercials, voiceovers, and industrials.
[SAG/AFTRA]

ABOUT ARTISTS AGENCY, INC.

1650 Broadway, Suite 1406, New York, NY 10019-6955
Telephone: 212-581-1857 **Website:** www.aboutartistsagency.com
E-Mail: mail@aboutartistsagency.com
Departments and Staff:
  Owner/Agent - Renee Glicker;
  Junior Agent - Joe Kokofsky; Assistant - Amelia Johnston
Ages Represented: 17+
Details: About Artists Agency represents a wide range of clientele
for film, TV, commercials, theatre, and specialty.
Tips: Applicants can submit headshots, resumes, and demo reels
by mail. Interviews are booked by appointment only. The agency
also accepts postcards and invitations.
[SAG/AFTRA, AEA, NATR]

ABOUT FACE TALENT

419 Park Ave South, Suite 607, New York, NY 10016
Telephone: 212-221-1518
E-Mail: aboutfacetalent@yahoo.com
Departments and Staff: Owner - Jeneviev Brewer;
  Associate - Alice Skiva;
  Assistant - Sonya Stewart
Details: This agency represents for theatre, film, TV, commercials,
voiceovers, industrials, commercial print, and trade shows.
[SAG/AFTRA, NATR]

ABRAMS ARTISTS AGENCY

275 7th Avenue, Floor 26, New York, NY 10001-6708
Telephone: 646-486-4600 **Website:** www.abramsartists.com
E-Mail: contactNY@abramsartists.com
Departments and Staff:
  Chairman/CEO - Harry Abrams;
  Senior Vice President - Neal Altma;
  Vice Presidents - Robert Attermann, Tracey Goldblum;
  Hosts/MCs/Broadcast/Reality TV - Mark Turner;
  Theatrical/Film/TV - Paul Reisman, Richard Fisher,
  Danielle Delawder, Samantha Stoller;
  Youth Division - Rachel Altman, Ellen Gilbert, Shelly
  Thompson, Bonnie Shumofsky;
  Commercials - Alison Quartin; Print - Joe Thompson;
  Voiceover - Jonathan Saul, Billy Serow, Jessica Felrice, Jenny
  Brown;
  Literary Division - Sarah Douglas, Charles Kopelman, Beth
  Blickers, Amy Wagner, Morgan Jenness, Ron Gwiazda, Peter
  Hagan, Steve Ross

NOTES

Details: This is a top ten agency. They provide services to both Los Angeles and New York City, and represent actors, dancers, musicians, writers, and sports figures, among many others.

Tips: Headshots and resumes are accepted by mail only. Interviews are granted by appointment only. Representatives also attend showcases.

[SAG/AFTRA, AEA, DGA, WGA, ATA, NATR]

ACCESS TALENT, INC.

171 Madison Avenue, Suite 1005, New York, NY 10016
Telephone: 212-331-9600 **Fax:** 212-684-8553
Website: www.accesstalent.com
E-Mail: projects@accesstalent.com
Departments and Staff:
    Co-Owners - Linda Weaver, Chas Cowing;
    Assistant Agent - Melissa McGee;
    Studio Manager - Chris Davis
Details: This agency specializes in voice talent.
Tips: CDs or MP3 files can be mailed or emailed along with a resume. Interviews are by appointment only.
[SAG/AFTRA, NON-UNION]

ACROSS THE BOARD TALENT AGENCY (ATB TALENT)

149 Madison Avenue, 11th Floor, New York, NY 10016
Telephone: 917-397-0282 **Fax:** 323-825-2281
Website: www.atbtalent.com
E-Mail: info@atbtalent.com
Departments and Staff: Founder - Guy Kochlani;
    VP of Talent - Todd M. Eskin
Details: This agency delivers a tailored client experience by staffing seasoned agents, while building a client roster of higher profile talent. ATB Talent has specialized departments including film/TV, theatre, and commercials.
Tips: Only hardcopy submissions accepted to be sent to the Woodland Hills, CA address for consideration in both New York and Los Angeles offices.Mark "New Faces" on the envelope.
[SAG/AFTRA, AEA, NON-UNION]

ADELE'S KIDS & ADULTS

33 Rupert Avenue, Staten Island, NY 10314
Telephone: 718-494-5000 **Website:** www.adeleskids.com
Departments and Staff: Owner - Adele Sharf
Email: adeleskids@gmail.com

Details: This agency works within the film, TV, commercial, print, and theatre disciplines.

Tips: All auditions/interviews are by appointment only. Children with an appointment will be seen Monday through Friday. Adults will be contacted by mail or phone.

AGENCY FOR THE PERFORMING ARTS, INC.

135 West 50th St., 17th Floor, New York, NY 10020
Telephone: 212-205-4320 **Fax:** 212-245-5062
Email: www.apa-agency.com   **Website:** www.apa-agency.com
Departments and Staff:
   Comedians - Michael Berkowitz, Marcus Levy, Andrew Russell, Tiffany Schloesser;
   Musical Artists - Andrew Buck, Alex Chaykin, Andrew Ellis, Fred Hansen, Lisa Hafer, Mike Selvin, and Josh Sherman;
   Talent - Barry McPherson;
   Branded Lifestyle - Megan Brown, P.J. Pierce
Details: This is a top ten agency. They are an international agency, with U.S. locations in Beverly Hills, New York City, and Nashville, represents artists in the film, TV, and theatre platforms. In addition, they represent comedians, musicians, and writers.
[SAG/AFTRA, WGA, DGA, AEA, AFM, ATA]

ANDREADIS TALENT AGENCY, INC.

119 W 57th Street, Suite 711, New York, NY 10019-2302
Telephone: 212-315-0303   **E-Mail:** andreadis@verizon.net
Departments and Staff:
   Owner/Agent - Barbara Andreadis;
   Assistants - Alex Stine, Yvette Rovira
Details: This agency represents talent of all ages for theatre, film, and TV.
Tips: Submissions should be sent by mail only and interviews will be held by appointment only. The agency will not accept unsolicited demos.
[SAG/AFTRA, AEA, NATR, NON-UNION]

ANN STEELE

330 W 42nd St Fl 18, New York, NY 10036-6902
Telephone: 212-629-9112   **Fax:** 212-629-9108
Website: annsteeleagency.com
E-Mail: ragtimeann@aol.com

Departments and Staff:
   Owner - Ann Steele
Details: This agency handles actors for film, TV, and theatre.
Tips: Industry referrals only.
[NATR, AFTRA, AEA]

ARCIERI & ASSOCIATES

6 East 39th Street, Suite 1202, New York, NY 10016
Telephone: 212-286-1700   **Fax:** 212-286-1110
Website: www.arcieritalent.com   **E-Mail:** info@arcieritalent.com
Departments and Staff:
   Owner/Agent - Steven Arcieri;
   Agents - Katie Bucco, Diana Lote;
   Assistant - Matt Brody
Details: This agency represents voiceover artists of all ages.
Tips: Resumes and demo recordings should be sent by email only.
Postcards and invitations are accepted.
[SAG/AFTRA, NATR]

ARTISTS GROUP, EAST INC.

1650 Broadway, Suite 1105, New York, NY 10019-6833
Telephone: 212-586-1452   **Fax:** 212-586-0037
Departments and Staff:
   Owner/Agent - Robert Malcolm
Details: The Artists Group, East, Inc. represents film, TV, and theatre performers.
Tips: Submissions accepted by mail only and interviews will be granted by appointment only.
[SAG/AFTRA, AEA]

ASSOCIATED BOOKING CORPORATION

501 Madison Avenue, #603, New York, NY 10022
Telephone: 212-874-2400   **Fax:** 212-769-3649
Website: www.associatedbooking.com
E-Mail: musicbiz@mindspring.com
Departments and Staff:
   President - Oscar Cohen;
   Vice President - Lisa Cohen
Details: This agency represents a variety of music artists.
Tips: Inquiries can be sent via email.

ATLAS TALENT AGENCY

15 E 32nd Street, Floor 6, New York, NY 10016-5423
Telephone: 212-730-4500 **Website:** www.atlastalent.com
E-Mail: jonn@atlastalent.com
Departments and Staff:
  Promos/Trailers/Documentaries/Animation - Jonn Wasser,
  Lisa Marber-Rich, John "Hoss" Hossenlopp, Heather Vergo,
  Ian Fisher, Priscila Torre, Rachel Goldman, Julia Pleasants;
  Commercial Voiceover - Tim Walsh, Carli Silver, Meredith,
  McKeon, Ricky Meyer, Mike, Milmore, Nick Lanza;
  On-Camera - Michael Guy, Noah Suchoff; Business Affairs -
  Just Richard, Ian Lesser, Jacker Garcia.
Details: Atlas Talent Agency handles clientele for commercials,
documentaries, and other promotional media. They have an
office on the west coast.
Tips: Headshots, resumes, demos, postcards, and invitations
can be sent via mail or email. The agency grants interviews by
appointment only.
[SAG/AFTRA, AEA, NATR, NON-UNION]

AVALON ARTISTS GROUP

242 W 30th Street, Suite 903, New York, NY 10001
Telephone: 212-868-3200 **Fax:** 212-868-3210
Website: www.avalonartists.com
E-Mail: craig@avalonartists.com
Departments and Staff: Owner - Craig Holzberg;
  Commercials - Michelle Thompson,Melinda Brown;
  Division Head of Youth - Bernadette McBrinn
Details: This agency works with actors, comedians, models,
and dancers. They represents all types for film, TV, theatre,
commercials, voiceovers, commercial print, and music videos.
Tips: Submissions are accepted. Though interviews are by
appointment only, agency representatives attend talent
showcases and will accept postcards and invitations.
[AEA, SAG/AFTRA, ATA, NATR]

BELLA AGENCY

270 Lafayette Street, Suite 802, New York, NY 10012
Telephone: 212-965-9200 **Fax:** 212-918-3467
Website: www.bellaagency.com
E-Mail: rvolant@bellaagency.com, twinslow@bellaagency.com
Departments and Staff:
  President - Ray Volant;
  Agents - Tom Winslow

Ages Represented: 18+

Details: They book for commercials and commercial print. Work with talent of all types and ethnicities.

Tips: Bella Agency does not conduct open calls. Photos can be submitted via the website. Do not send submissions directly to agents.

BLOC TALENT AGENCY, NY

630 9th Avenue, Suite 702, New York, NY 10036-3747
Telephone: 212-924-6200 **Fax:** 212-924-6280
Website: www.nyc.blocagency.com
E-Mail: info.nyc@blocagency.com
Departments and Staff:
  Commercials -Emily Watson, Fatima Wilson; Film/TV - Jim Daly;
  Junior Agent - Maegan Mishico

Details: This bicoastal agency represents dancers, choreographers, musical theatre artists, sports personalities, martial arts, and stunts performers.

Tips: Interested parties should fill out an online submission form or mail a headshot, resume, and cover letter. The agency holds general auditions each year and attends classes, workshops, showcases, and area performances. Interviews will be granted by appointment only.

[SAG/AFTRA, AEA]

BMG MODELS

242 W 30th Street, Suite 903, New York, NY 10001
Telephone: 212-279-6800 **Website:** www.bmgmodels.com
E-Mail: newyork@bmgmodels.com
Departments and Staff: Agents - Erica Moran, Rickey Kalinowski
Details: A sister agency of Avalon Artists Group, BMG Models represents models of all ages not only for commercials, print, and runway, but also for film and TV.

Tips: An open call for print models is held every Thursday afternoon. Online and print applications are accessible via the agency's website.

[SAG/AFTRA]

BOSS MODELS

227 E 56th Street, 3rd Floor, Suite 301, New York, NY 10022
Telephone: 212-242-2444 **Fax:** 212-242-5554
Website: bossmodels.com

E-Mail: info@bossmodels.com
Details: This agency represents young talent (specializing in ages 15-24) for print and fashion events.
Tips: Submissions are accepted from around the world. Those interested should send photos via email with the subject line "New Faces." Open calls are also held every Wednesday afternoon.

BRET ADAMS, LTD

448 W 44th Street, New York, NY 10036-5205
Telephone: 212-765-5630 **Fax:** 212-265-2212
Website: www.bretadamsltd.net
E-Mail: bretadamsltd@bretadamsltd.net
Departments and Staff:
   Partners - Bruce Ostler (Literary),
   Ken Melamed (Acting), Margi Rountree (Acting);
   Acting Associates - Alexis Williams, Colin Hunt;
   Acting Assistant - Emily Snyder; Literary Agent - Mark
   Orsini
Details: This is a top ten agency. Bret Adams, LTD represents a talent base consisting of writers, composers, directors, choreographers, and actors in the film, TV, and theatre arenas.
Tips: Headshots and resumes may be submitted by mail only. Interviews will be held by appointment only.
[SAG/AFTRA, AEA, WGA, ATA, NATR]

BRS/GAGE TALENT AGENCY

1650 Broadway, Suite 1410, New York, NY 10019-6957
Telephone: 212-757-0098 **Fax:** 212-489-8531
Website: www.brsgage.com/ **Email:** brsgage@gmail.com
Departments and Staff:
   Partners-Mark Redanty, David Shaul, Martin Gage
   Talent Agensts- Amy Abell-Rosenfield, Phil Adelman,
   Charles Bodner, Adam Lazarus, Erika Karnell, Steven Unger
   NY Assistants - Chris Horsman, Kristin Lavo
Details: This firm represents film and TV actors.
Tips: No unsolicited submissions are accepted. Industry referrals only.

[SAG/AFTRA, AEA, NATR, ATA]

CARLTON, GODDARD, AND FREER TALENT

352 7th Avenue, Suite 1601, New York, NY 10001
Telephone: 212-379-6822 **Website:** cfgtalent.com
E-Mail: submissions@cgstalent.com
Departments and Staff:
   Partners - Joel Carlton, Michael Goddard, Christopher Freer

NOTES

Ages Represented: 18+
Details: This agency represents directors, choreographers, and actors for film, TV, and theatre.
Tips: Headshots and resumes can be submitted by mail or email. Interviews are held by appointment only.
[AEA, NATR]

CARMEN HAND MODEL MGMT.

209 E 56th Street, Suite 12N, New York, NY 10022
Telephone: 212-758-1188
Website: www.carmenhandmodels.com
E-Mail: carmenhandmodelMGMT@gmail.com
Departments and Staff:
    Owner - Carmen Marrufo
Details: Represents actors and models for hand and body part modeling. They have a "Kids" division.

CARRY CO. TALENT

20 W 20th Street, Floor 2, New York, NY 10011-9260
Telephone: 212-768-2793 **Fax:** 646-349-2250
Website: www.carrycompany.com
Departments and Staff:
    Owner/Agent - Sharon Carry;
    Assistant - Amanda Keith
Details: The Carry Company represents talent of all ages for commercials, film, and TV.
Tips: Submissions should be sent by mail. Do not send unsolicited tapes. Phone calls and walk-ins are not allowed.
[SAG/AFTRA, AEA, WGA]

CARSON ADLER AGENCY, INC.

250 W 57th Street, Suite 2128, New York, NY 10107-2013
Telephone: 212-307-1882   **Website:** www.carsonadler.com
Departments and Staff:
    Owner/Agent - Nancy Carson;
    Agents - Bonnie Deroski, Shirley Faison
Ages Represented: 4-Early 20's
Details: This agency represents children and young adults for film, TV, voiceovers, and theatre.
Tips: Headshots, resumes, demos, and reels can be submitted by mail or on their website. Those who are contacted for an interview will audition onsite.
[NATR, AEA, SAG/AFTRA]

CARSON KOLKER ORGANIZATION

419 Park Avenue South, Suite 606, New York, NY 10016-8410
Telephone: 212-221-1517 **Fax:** 212-221-1605
E-Mail: barrypeter@kolkerorg.com
Departments and Staff:
    Owners/Agents - Barry Kolker, Jenevieve Brewer;
    Agents - Alice Skiba, Huascar Vizcaino;
    Associate - Sonia Stewart
Details: This agency represents talent of all ages for print, broadcast, fashion, sports, dance, voiceovers, theatre, film, and TV.
Tips: Submissions should be sent by mail only. Interviews will be granted by appointment only.
[SAG/AFTRA, AEA, NATR]

CHOICE MODELS & TALENT AGENCY

505 Eighth Avenue, Suite 802, New York, NY 10018
Telephone: 212-239-3539
Departments and Staff: CEO - Artie Regan
Details: They represent models, actors, and singers for print, commercials, film, and TV.
Tips: No unsolicited submissions are allowed.

CLEAR TALENT GROUP

325 W 38th Street, Suite 1203, New York, NY 10018-9700
Telephone: 212-840-4100 **Fax:** 212-967-4567
Website: www.cleartalentgroup.com
E-Mail: nyinfo@cleartalentgroup.com
Departments and Staff:
    Agent/Director of Operations in NY - Jamie Harris;
    Agents - Justin Busch, Julianna Lichtman
Ages Represented: 18+
Details: Clear Talent Group represents models, actors, directors, designers, dancers, and choreographers for film, TV, theatre, commercials, and more.
Tips: Interested parties should send submissions via mail, email, or online application.
[SAG/AFTRA, AEA, ATA, WGA]

CLICK MODEL - NEW YORK

129 W 27th Street, Penthouse, New York, NY 10001
Telephone: 212-206-1616 (Women), 212-206-1717 (Men)

NOTES

Fax: 212-206-6228
Website: www.clickmodel.com   **E-Mail:** clickmodel@aol.com
Details: This agency represents models for runway, fashion print, and commercials. They work with plus size models.
Tips: Applicants can send photos by mail or fill out the online application form. There is also an open call on Friday afternoons.

COLUMBIA ARTISTS MANAGEMENT

5 Columbus Circle @ 1790 Broadway, 6th Floor
New York, NY 10019-1412
Telephone: 212-841-9500   **Fax:** 212-841-9744
Website: www.cami.com   **E-Mail:** info@cami.com
Departments and Staff:
Details: This agency represents dancers, vocalists, musicians, and fine arts productions.

CORNERSTONE

37 W 20th Street, Suite 1108, New York, NY 10011
Telephone: 212-807-8344   **Fax:** 212-807-8662
E-Mail: cstonetalent@earthlink.net
Departments and Staff: Agents - Steve Stone, Mark Schlegel;
    Assistant - Shannon Kelly
Details: They represent actors in film, TV, and theatre.
Tips: Headshots and resumes can be submitted by mail or email. Interviews are held by appointment only.
[SAG/AFTRA, AEA, NATR]

CREATIVE ARTISTS AGENCY

405 Lexington Avenue, 19th Floor, New York, NY 10174
Telephone: 212-277-9000   **Fax:** 212-277-9099
Website: www.caa.com   **E-Mail:** info@caa.com
Departments and Staff:
    President - Richard Lovett;
    Agents - Mackenzie Condon, Corinne Hayoun, Katie Maloney, Adam Nettler;
    TV - Olivia Metzger, Jason Fox, Eric Wattenberg, CC Hirsch, Scott Lonker, Andrea Ross;
    Theatre - George Lane, Olivier Sultan, Joe Machota, Chris Till;
    Music - Stephanie Mahler, Brian Manning, Mario Tirado, Nat Farnham, Scott Morris, Mark Cheatham
Details: This is a top five agency. CAA represents a client list of performers, writers, and speakers over a wide assortment of disciplines, including broadcast, film, TV, theatre, voiceovers, commercials, and publishing with offices on the west coast.
Tips: Industry referrals only. No submissions.

[SAG/AFTRA, AEA, ATA, DGA,WGA]

CUNNINGHAM-ESCOTT-SLEVIN-DOHERTY TALENT AGENCY

333 7th Avenue, 11th Floor, New York, NY 10001
Telephone: 212-477-1666   **Fax:** 212-473-1594
Website: www.cesdtalent.com   **E-Mail:** info@cesdtalent.com
Departments and Staff:
   President - Ken Slevin;
   Commercials/Hosting - Kirsten Walther;
   Commercials - Maura Maloney, Lakey Wolff;
   Beauty/Dance - Jessie Krysko, Jill Borst;
   Voiceover - Tom Celia, Anita Reilly;
   Promos/Trailer Narrations/Hosting - Donna Mancino;
   Imaging for Radio and TV - Nate Zeitz; Youth - Erin Grush,
   Mara Glauberg; Adult Print - Lindsay Glickman
Details: CESD Talent Agency represents a variety of talent in the film, TV, theatre, dance, print, commercial, and voiceover arenas.
Tips: Headshots and resumes can be submitted via mail or dropoff. Choreography DVDs and links to voiceover files are also accepted. Interviews are by appointment only.
[SAG/AFTRA, ATA, NATR, NACA]

DDO ARTIST AGENCY

175 Varick Street, Suite #268, New York, NY 10014
Telephone: 212-379-6314   **Fax:** 646-519-4279
Website: www.ddoagency.com   **E-Mail:** nyc@ddoagency.com
Departments and Staff:
   Director/Theatrical/Dance and Choreography - Thomas Scott;
   Commercials - Jerry Kallarakkal
Ages Represented: 18+
Details: This agency represents talent of all ages in print, film, TV, sports, and especially dance and choreography. They have an office on the west coast.
Tips: Headshots and resumes are accepted by mail or email. Interviews will be granted by appointment only.
[SAG/AFTRA, AEA]

DNA MODELS

555 W 25th Street, 6th Floor, New York, NY 10001
Telephone: 212-226-0080   **Fax:** 212-226-1199
Website: www.dnamodels.com
E-Mail: info@dnamodels.com,
submission.women@dnamodels.com,
submission.men@dnamodels.com

NOTES

Departments and Staff:
Men's Agents - Gene Kogan, Matthew Trust, Austin Rubino, Carlotta Sironi, Kadeem Johnson;
Women's Agents - Didier Fernandez, Lorenzo Re, Valerie Bullen, Greg Fricke, Akeem Rasool, Richie Keo, Butterfly Cayley, Helena Suric
Details: This agency works with models.
Tips: Submit by email or mail with subject line "New Faces."

DON BUCHWALD AND ASSOCIATES

10 E 44th Street, New York, NY 10017-3601
Telephone: 212-867-1200   **Fax:** 212-687-7706
Website: www.buchwald.com   **E-Mail:** info@buchwald.com
Departments and Staff:
President/CEO - Don Buchwald;
COO/Business Affairs for Film/TV/Theatre - Richard Basch;
Vice Presidents - Ricki Olshan, Robyn Stecher, Stephen Fisher;
Legit Agents - Elizabeth Wiederseim, Joanne Nici, Stephanie Bellarosa, Alan Willig, David Lewis, Jonathan Mason;
Commercial/Voiceover Agents - David Elliott, Michael Raymen, Robyn Starr, Pamela Goldman, Katherine Ryan;
Broadcast Agents - Eric Winchel, Tony Burton;
Children's Agent - Victoria Kress
Details: This is a top ten agency. They represent writers, models, speakers, directors, and actors of all ages for film, TV, theatre, broadcast, and print.
Tips: Submit headshots and resumes by mail only. Postcards and invitations accepted.
[SAG/AFTRA, AEA, DGA, ATA]

DOUGLAS, GORMAN, ROTHACKER AND WILHELM, INC.

33 W 46th Street, Suite 801, New York, NY 10036
Telephone: 212-382-2000   **Fax:** 212-719-2878
Website: www.dgrwinc.com   **E-Mail:** info@dgrwinc.com
Departments and Staff: Executive - Jim Wilhelm;
Agents - Josh Pultz
Ages Represented: 18+
Details: They book dancers, directors, choreographers, and actors for film, TV, and theatre.
Tips: Headshots and resumes accepted via mail. They will not take unsolicited demos. Interviews by appointment only.
[SAG/AFTRA, AEA, AGVA, NATR]

DULCINA EISEN & ASSOCIATES

154 E 61st Street, New York, NY 10065-8507
Telephone: 212-355-6617 **E-Mail:** eisenagents@gmail.com
Departments and Staff: Owner - Dulcina Eisen;
Ages Represented: 18+
Details: Book actors for film, TV, and theatre.
Tips: Industry referrals preferred, though they will accept headshots, resumes, postcards, and invitations by mail only. Interviews by appointment only.
[SAG/AFTRA, AEA]

EILEEN HAVES TALENT REPRESENTATIVE

416 East 85th Street, H4E, New York, NY 10028
Telephone: 212-249-0033 **E-Mail:** eyhaves@yahoo.com
Departments and Staff: Owner - Eileen Haves
Ages Represented: 20+
Details: This agency will work with talent for commercials and industrials.
[AEA, SAG/AFTRA, NATR]

ELITE MODELS

245 Fifth Avenue, 24th Floor, New York, NY 10016
Telephone: 212-529-9700 **Fax:** 212-475-0572
Website: www.elitemodel.com **E-Mail:** info@elitemodel.com
Details: This well-established agencey works with models.
Tips: Submit by email or drop-off with subject line "New Faces."

ENVY MODEL & TALENT

244 W 54th Street, Suite 614 Studio A, New York, NY 10019
Telephone: 917-438-0878
Website: www.envymodelmanagement.com
E-Mail: envynyc@envymodelmanagement.com,
        daniel@theenvyagency.com
Departments and Staff:
    Daniel Mahan;
    Women/Men - Andrew Borquez; New Faces - Barbara King
Details: This bicoastal agency represents both models and actors of all ages and types for runway, fashion print, editorial, commercials, film, TV.
Tips: Submit materials by email.
[SAG/AFTRA, NON-UNION]

NOTES

EXPECTING MODELS, INC.

470 7th Ave, Suite 404, New York, NY 10018
Telephone: 212-473-5152 **Fax:** 917-591-6744
Website: www.expectingmodels.com
E-Mail: liza@expectingmodels.com, traci@expectingmodels.com
Departments and Staff:
   Director- Traci Jackson
Details: Expecting actors and mothers and their families are represented here for commericals and print modeling. Children under the age of five are also represented.
Tips: Complete the online submission form to be considered for representation.
[SAG/AFTRA]

FIFI OSCARD AGENCY

110 W 40th Street, 16th Floor, Room #704,
New York, NY 10018-8512
Telephone: 212-764-1100 **Fax:** 212-840-5019
Website: www.fifioscard.com **E-Mail:** agency@fifioscard.com
Departments and Staff:
   VP/Talent - Carmen La Via;
   TV/Feature/Theatre - Francis Del Duca;
   Commercials/Voiceover/Print - Kevin McShane;
   Commercials/Voiceover/Print/Children - Scott Smith;
   Literary Agents - Peter Sawyer, Carmen La Via, Carolyn French, Kevin McShane, Ivy Fischer Stone, Jerome Rudes, Laura R. Paperny
Ages Represented: 8+
[SAG/AFTRA, WGA]

FLAUNT MODEL & TALENT, INC.

35 West 35th Street, Suite 901, New York, NY 10001
Telephone: 212-679-9011 **Fax:** 212-679-0938
Website: www.flauntmodels.com
E-Mail: submissions@flauntmodels.com
Departments and Staff:
   President - Gene Roseman;
   Talent Coordinator - Winnie Riheldaffer
Details: They work with actors and models for commercials, commercial print, showroom, and trade shows. Their modeling division also books for shoe modeling.
Tips: Submit photos and stats via email or mail. No drop-ins.

FORD MODELS/COMMERCIAL PRINT DIVISION

11 East 26th Street, 14th Floor, New York, NY 10010
Telephone: 212-219-6500 **Fax:** 212-960-5028
Website: www.fordmodels.com   **E-Mail:** lifestyle@fordmodels.com
Departments and Staff:
    CEO- Katie Ford
    Founder- Eileen Ford
    Talent Agenst- Kamia Butler, Jeff Andrews, Anthony Hernandez
Ages Represented: 18+
Details: The commercial print division of Ford Models that works with teens, adults, and seniors. There are also locations in Chicago, Miami, and Los Angeles.
Tips: To apply, complete the online submission form. Interviews are granted by appointment only.

FRONTIER BOOKING INTERNATIONAL

1441 Broadway, Suite 1500, New York, NY 10018
Telephone: 212-221-0220 **Website:** www.frontierbooking.com
E-Mail: john@frontierbooking.com
Departments and Staff: Film/TV/Commercials - John Shea;
    Commercials/Voiceover - Heather Finn
Ages Represented: Infants-30's
Details: Frontier is a full-service talent agency that represents children and young adults of all ethnicities. They book for actors, models, singers, designers, and voiceover artists.
Tips: Please mail photos and resumes. Phone calls and drop-ins will not be accepted.
[SAG/AFTRA. AEA]

FUNNYFACE TODAY MODELS

381 Park Ave South, Room 821, New York, NY 10016
Telephone: 212-686-4343 **Website:** www.fftmodels.com
E-Mail: fft@fftmodels.com
Departments and Staff:
    President - Jane Blum;
    Men - Lavina Gonzalez; Adults - Charlie Winfield;
    Kids - Doris Stinga, Fabiola Osorio
Details: They represent all ages for film, TV, commercials, and print.
Tips: Apply by completing the online submissions page. Interviews are conducted by appointment only.

GARBER TALENT

521 5th Avenue, Suite 1700, New York, NY 10175
Telephone: 212-292-4910
Departments and Staff: Owner - Karen S. Garber
Ages Represented: 18+
Details: They book talent for broadcast, voiceovers, commercials, film, and TV.
Tips: Application materials can be sent by mail only. Interviews are conducted by appointment only.
[SAG/AFTRA, AEA]

GENERATION TV, LLC

20 W 20th Street, Suite 1008, New York, NY 10011-9252
Telephone: 212-727-7219 **Fax:** 212-727-7147
Website: www.generationmm.com
E-Mail: info@generationmm.com
Departments and Staff:
    Owner- Patti Fleischer
    Agent -Mallory Levy, Dina Torre
Ages Represented: Up to age 21
Details: This agency is the acting division of Generation Model Management. They represent children and young adults for commercials, TV series, theatre, or film.
Tips: Submissions accepted by mail. They accept snapshots (for children) and demo reels. Interviews by appointment only; no calls or drop-ins.
[SAG/AFTRA, AEA]

GERSH LITERARY & TALENT AGENCY

41 Madison Avenue, 33rd Floor, New York, NY 10010
Telephone: 212-997-1818 **Fax:** 212-997-1978
Website: www.gershagency.com **E-Mail:** info@gershla.com
Departments and Staff:
    VPs - Rhonda Price, Stephen Hirsh;
    Talent Coordinator - Scott Swiontek;
    Agents - Kyetay Beckner, Randi Goldstein, Jason Gutman, Val McKeon, Lindsay Porter, Mira Young
Details: This is a top ten agency. They represents talent for film, TV, and theatre.
Tips: This agency only accepts industry referrals.
[AEA, SAG/AFTRA, ATA, NATR, DGA, WGA]

NOTES

GONZALEZ MODEL & TALENT AGENCY

112 East 23rd Street Penthouse, New York, NY 10010-4518
Telephone: 212-982-5626 **Website:** www.gonzalezmodels.com
E-Mail: info@gonzalezmodels.com
Departments and Staff:
    Owner - Rick Gonzalez
Ages Represented: 5+
Details: They book for commercials, print, industrials, fashion, film, and TV.
Tips: Submissions can be sent via mail or email. Interviews are conducted by appointment only.

GOTHAM TALENT AGENCY

570 Seventh Avenue, Room 1001, New York, NY 10018-1611
Telephone: 212-944-8898 **Fax:** 212-944-8899
Website: www.gothamtalentagency.com
E-Mail: submissions@gothamtalentagency.com
Departments and Staff:
    Agent - Cynthia Katz
Ages Represented: 16+
Details: The clients at this agency are seen for film, TV, theatre, and commercials.
Tips: Please send submissions through mail.
[SAG/AFTRA, AEA, NATR]

HANNS WOLTERS

501 Fifth Avenue, #2112A, New York, NY 10017-8612
Telephone: 212-714-0100 **Website:** www.hannswolters.com
E-Mail: hannsw@aol.com
Departments and Staff:
    Owner - Oliver Mahrdt;
    Assistant - Bill Duey
Details: Specializes in American and Foreign talent and off-beat types. They book for motion pictures, TV, commercials, and have a voiceover department specializing in all foreign languages. The Agency also represents writers, producers, directors, and even corporations.
Tips: Send headshot, resume, and cover letter by mail. Will not accept demos and scripts unless they are requested. Twitter: @ hannswolters; Facebook: Hanns Wolters International Inc.
[SAG/AFTRA, AEA]

NOTES

HARDEN-CURTIS ASSOCIATES

214 W 29th Street, Suite 1203, New York, NY 10001
Telephone: 212-977-8502 **Website:** www.hardencurtis.com
E-Mail: hcassc@hardencurtis.com
Departments and Staff:
  Owners - Mary Harden, Nancy Curtis;
  Agents - Diane Riley, Michael Kirsten, Scott D. Edwards,
  Joanna Bell Koster;
  Assistants - Marianne Broome, Courtney Beam
Details: This agency does not represent children, but represents
adults actors and writers for film, TV, and theatre (musical or
otherwise). They also represent writer, directors, dancers, and
choreographers.
Tips: Please submit through mail with a self-addressed stamped
envelope for response.
[SAG/AFTRA, AEA, NATR]

HARTIG-HILEPO AGENCY, LTD.

54 W 21st Street, Room 610, New York, NY 10010-7344
Telephone: 212-929-1772 **Fax:** 212-929-1772
Website: www.hartighilepo.com
E-Mail: info@hartighilepo.com
Departments and Staff:
  Owner/Agent - Paul Hilepo;
  Agents - Liz Rosier, Peter Sanfilippo;
  Assistants - Katie Simpson, Aaron Sandler
Details: They work with actors and adolescents for theatre, film,
and TV. This agency does not work with children.
Tips: Submit via mail or e-mail. They work with freelance, union,
and non-union talent. No phone calls or drop-offs.
[SAG/AFTRA, AEA, NATR]

HEADLINE TALENT

250 Greenwich Street, New York, NY 10007
Telephone: 212-257-6110 **Fax:** 646-786-6811
Website: headlinetalent.net
E-Mail: emily@headlinetalent.net
Departments and Staff:
  Director of Talent - Erica Bines;
  Talent Agent - Lisa Lawrence; Junior Talent Agent - Ben
  Jordon Lawrence, Antonio Servidio;
  Assistant - Ben Jordon
Details: This agency works with actors and writers for film, TV,
theatre, and hosting.

Tips: This agency only accepts industry referrals.
[ATA]

HENDERSON/HOGAN AGENCY

850 7th Avenue, Suite 1003, New York, NY 10019-5230
Telephone: 212-765-5190 **Fax:** 212-586-2855
E-Mail: hendersonhogan@gmail.com
Departments and Staff: President - George Lutsch;
    Agent - Alex Butler, Chad Pisetsky
    Assistant - Rachel Wagner
Details: This agency represents actors for film, TV, and theatre (including musical performers). Also represents comedians and dancers.
Tips: Do not personally drop anything off, call for an inquiry, and interviews are by appointment only.
[SAG/AFTRA, AEA]

IMAGES MODEL MANAGEMENT

900 Broadway, Suite 605, New York, NY 10003
Telephone: 212-228-0300 **Fax:** 212-228-0438
Website: www.imagesnyc.com **E-Mail:** images@imagesnyc.com
Departments and Staff: President - Kathy Geraghty;
    Women/Men - Dani Bongiorno; Men - Philip Kearney;
    Women - Gary Bertalovitz
Ages Represented: 15+
Details: They represent talent for film, TV, commercials, commercial print, and beauty.

IMG MODELS

304 Park Avenue South, Penthouse North, New York, NY 10010
Telephone: 212-253-8884 **Fax:** 212-253-8883
Website: www.imgmodels.com **E-Mail:** modelinfo@imgworld.com
Details: Represents models for runway, print, and commercials. They also work with sports personalities.
Tips: Submit by email with subject line "New Faces." or via the "Get Scouted" link on the website.

INGBER & ASSOCIATES

1140 Broadway, Room 907, New York, NY 10001-7693
Telephone: 212-889-9450 **Fax:** 221-779-0490
E-Mail: caroleingber@ingberassoc.com

NOTES

Departments and Staff:
    Owner/Agent - Carole R. Ingber
    Talent Assistant - Sam Catapano
Ages Represented: 18+
Details: Talent are represented primarily in commercials, voiceover and industrials.
Tips: This agency accepts headshots and resumes through mail; audition tapes, CDs, or voiceover demos will not be returned. They do not accept phone calls.
[SAG/AFTRA, AEA, NATR]

INNOVATIVE ARTISTS

235 Park Avenue South, Floor 10, New York, NY 10003-1405
Telephone: 212-253-6900   **Fax:** 212-253-1198
Website: www.innovativeartists.com   **E-Mail:** talent@iany.com
Departments and Staff:
    Vice President/Talent - Gary Gersh;
    Vice President/Commercials- Maury DiMauro;
    Talent - Allison Levy, Lisa Lieberman, Brian C. Davidson, Kenneth Lee, Bill Veloric;
    On-Camera - Michael Shera, Marla Haut, Liz Klausner, Barbara Coleman;
    Breakout - Jaime Misher, Katie McGrath;
    Beauty - Ross Haime, Nipa Parikh, Christin Whitelaw, Scott Kenyon;
    Voiceover - Debra Sherry, Allan G. Duncan, Eileen Schellhorn, Shari Hoffman
Details: This is a top ten agency. They are a large agency that represents children and adults for film. TV, voiceover, and commercials. They also have divisions for hosting, comedians, and writers. They have offices in Chicago and Los Angeles.
Tips: This agency only accepts industry referrals.
[ATA, SAG/AFTRA, AEA]

INTERNATIONAL ARTISTS GROUP, INC.

34 W 86th Street, Suite B, New York, NY 10024
Telephone: 786-277-6108, 646-370-6837
E-Mail: meris007@hotmail.com
Departments and Staff:
    Owner - Meris Zittman
Details: This agency specializes in representation for Hispanic and ethnic talent. They work with all ages in print, theatre, film, TV, and commercials.
[SAG/AFTRA]

ICM PARTNERS

730 5th Avenue, Floor 3, New York, NY 10019-4148
Telephone: 212-556-5600   **Fax:** 212-556-5665
Website: www.icmpartners.com
E-Mail: careersny@icmtalent.com
Departments and Staff:
    Partners - Lisa Bankoff, Christina Bazdekis, Kimberly Behzadi, Bonnie Bernstein, Mitch Blackman, Boaty Boatwright, Steven Brown, Ayala Cohen, Kristine Dahl, Diana Glazer, Shade Grant, Sloan Harris, Patrick Herold, Zach Iser, Sarah R. Kelly, Sean Liebowitz, Kristine Marshall, Esther Newberg, Josh Pearl, Liz Pokora-Sadowsky, Adam Schweitzer, Mark Siegel, Nick Storch, Lawrence Stuart, Amanda Urban, Bart Walker, Lori Yorkrt Walker, Joanne Wiles, Eddy Yablans, Lori York
Details: ICM Partners is one of the world's largest talent and literary agencies, with offices in Los Angeles, New York, Washington, D.C. and London. A cornerstone of the entertainment industry for more than three decades, ICM Partners represents creative and technical talent in the fields of motion pictures, television, music, publishing, live performance, branded entertainment and new media. Under the leadership of partners from each of the agency's core areas of business, ICM Partners continues actively to seek new opportunities for its clients as emerging technologies reshape the media landscape.
Tips: This agency only accepts industry referrals. Unsolicited submissions will not be accepted.
[AFM, DGA, WGA, ATA, AGVA, AFTRA, AEA]

IPM MODEL MANAGEMENT

304 Park Avenue South, 11th Floor, New York, NY 10010
Telephone: 212-213-1977   **Fax:** 646-792-4869
Website: www.ipmmodels.com
E-Mail: newfaces@ipmmodels.com
Departments and Staff:
    CEO President - Fallon Sinclair;
    Agents - Kassie Jones, Toi English
Details: This agency represents models size 4-16 including plus size female models for commercial print, fashion, runway, and TV. There are also locations in Los Angeles and Miami.
Tips: Submit by completing the online application or sending photos via email.

JAN ALPERT MODEL MANAGEMENT

333 East 55th Street, Suite 7-G, New York, NY 10022
Telephone: 212-223-4238 **Fax:** 212-223-9244
Website: www.janalpertmodelmanagement.com
E-Mail: david@janalpertmodels.com
Departments and Staff:
 Owner/Agent - Jan Alpert;
 Agent - David Roos
Details: Represents for commercials, print, fashion, and trade shows.
Tips: This agency works with non-union talent.

JORDAN GILL & DORNBAUM

1370 Broadway, 5th Floor, New York, NY 10018
Telephone: 212-463-8455 **Fax:** 212-691-6111
Website: www.jgdtalent.com **E-Mail:** jgdtalent@aol.com
Departments and Staff:
 Owners - Robin Dornbaum, Jeffrey J. Gill;
 Commercials - David McDermott
Ages Represented: 4-25 for Theatre, TV, Film. All ages for commercials.
Details: This agency represents children and young adults in commercials, TV, film, voiceovers, industrials, live promotions, and theatre. They also have a small division that represents adults and seniors for commercials.
Tips: Send all submissions through mail. Children under the age of 4 do not require professional photos. They do not accept phone inquiries or drop-ins. They will contact you within two weeks if they are interested.
[SAG/AFTRA, AEA, NATR]

JUDY BOALS, INC.

307 W 38th Street, Room 812, New York, NY 10018-3533
Telephone: 212-500-1425 **Fax:** 212-500-1426
Website: www.judyboals.com **E-Mail:** info@judyboals.com
Departments and Staff:
 Owner/Agent - Judy Boals;
 Agents - Ann Kelly, Jenna Winnett
Ages Represented: 18+
Details: This literary and talent agency represents writers for film, TV, and theatre (including musicals). They also represent comedians, hosts & MCs, directors, voiceover artists, and dancers.

Tips: This agency will accept submissions by mail and e-mail. Interviews are by appointment only; no calls or drop-offs accepted.
[SAG/AFTRA, AEA]

KAZARIAN/MEASURES/RUSKIN & ASSOCIATES (KMR)

110 West 40th, Suite #2506, New York, NY 10018
Telephone: 212-582-7572 **Fax:** 212-582-7448
Website: www.KMRtalent.com
Details: This agency books actors for theatre, film, and TV. They also have a location in Studio City, CA.
Tips: Submit a headshot, resume, cover letter by mail. The agency doesn't accept unsolicited DVD demos. Interviews are held by appointment only.
[NATR, SAG/AFTRA, AEA]

KEIN-GOLDBERG . & ASSOCIATES

155 E 55th Street, Suite 5D, New York, NY 10022-4038
Telephone: 212-838-7373
E-Mail: ckaoffice@nyc.rr.com, kgatalent@nyc.rr.com
Departments and Staff:
　　Owner - Charles Kerin; Ellie Goldberg
　　Agents - Norman Meranus, Ronald Ross
Details: They represent all ages of clientele, including writers, composers, musicians, designers, directors, dancers, choreographers, and variety artists for film, TV, theatre, print, broadcast, and voiceovers.
Tips: Headshots and resumes should be sent via mail. No walk-ins allowed.
[SAG/AFTRA, AEA, NATR, WGA]

THE KRASNY OFFICE

1501 Broadway, Suite 1507, New York, NY 10019
Telephone: 212-730-8160 **E-Mail:** gary@thekrasnyoffice.com
Departments and Staff:
　　Owner - Gary Krasny;
　　Agents - B. Lynne Jebens, Mikey Nagy
Ages Represented: 18+
Details: This agency represents talent for film, TV, and theatre.
Tips: Send headshots and resumes by mail. Interviews will be held by appointment only.
[SAG/AFTRA, AEA]

NOTES

LALLY TALENT

630 9th Avenue, Suite 800, New York, NY 10036-3746
Telephone: 212-974-8718   **E-Mail:** ltaskaking@aol.com
Departments and Staff:
  Owners - Dale R. Lally, Stephen Laviska;
Ages Represented: 18+
Details: They represent actors and musical talent in theatre, film, and TV.
Tips: They only consider mailed submissions and will follow up with a scheduled interview if interested. Do not phone or drop-in.
[SAG/AFTRA, AEA, NATR, AGVA]

LAUREN GREEN AGENCY

54 West 21st Street, Suite 1206, New York, NY 10010
Telephone: 212-808-0777   **Fax:** 212-808-0011
Website: www.laurengreenagency.com
E-Mail: newtalent@lgmodels.com
Departments and Staff:
  Owner - Lauren Green
  Talent Agent - Caitlyn Dowdy
Details: Represents for for commercial and commercial print. They are looking for new talent of all ages and ethnicities.
Tips: They accept submissions by email at newtalent@lgmodels.com.

LEADING ARTISTS, INC.

145 W 45th Street, Suite 1000, New York, NY 10036
Telephone: 212-391-4545   **Fax:** 212-354-4941
E-Mail: dianne@leadingart.com
Departments and Staff:
  Owner - Dianne Busch;
  Assistants - Michael Kelly Boone, Diana Doussant, Danny Laraway, Mike Francis
Details: This agency works exclusively with actors in the areas of film, TV, and theatre.
Tips: Headshots and resumes are accepted by mail only. Do not submit unsolicited demos. Interviews will be granted by appointment only.
[AEA, SAG/AFTRA, NATR]

LIONEL LARNER LTD.

119 W 57th Street, #1412, New York, NY 10019-2303
Telephone: 212-246-3105   **E-Mail:** lionel.larner@mac.com, lionellarner@aol.com

LISA LAX AGENCY

1345 Avenue of the Americas, 2nd Floor, New York, NY 10105
Telephone: 646-648-0138, 901-246-8249
Website: www.lisalaxagency.com
E-Mail: lisalax@mac.com
Departments and Staff:
 Owner/Heads Memphis Office - Lisa Lax;
 NY Office - Terry Neil Edlefsen
 Assistant - Valerie Curtis
Details: This agency initially began in Memphis, TN and the New York offices of this agency open in September of 2011. They are now looking for experienced talent to work in film, TV, and theatre.
Tips: This agency accepts resumes and professional headshots by email. No phone calls, please.

LUEDTKE AGENCY

1674 Broadway, Suite 7A, New York, NY 10019-5855
Telephone: 212-765-9564 **Fax:** 212-765-9582
E-Mail: luedtke@luedtkeagency.com
Departments and Staff:
 Owner - Penny Luedtke
 Associates - Jessica Morgulis, Mike Cruz
Details: This agency works in the areas of TV, film, theatre, and commercials. They have booked work for many top of the line TV programs.
Tips: Submissions should be sent by mail. Interviews will be granted by appointment only.
[AFM, ATA, AGVA, SAG/AFTRA, AEA, AGMA]

MAJOR MODEL MANAGEMENT

419 Park Ave South, Suite 1201, New York, NY 10016
Telephone: 212-685-1200 **Fax:** 212-683-5200
Website: www.majormodel.com **E-Mail:** info@majormodel.com
Departments and Staff:
President - Katia Sherman
Details: Represents models for runway, fashion print, and commercials.
Tips: Photos are accepted via mail and email. Interested parties may also attend open calls on the first Wednesday of every month.

MARILYN MODEL MANAGEMENT

32 Union Square East, Penthouse, New York, NY 10003
Telephone: 212-260-6500 **Fax:** 646-478-9739

Website: www.Marilynagency.com **E-Mail:** info@marilyn-ny.com
Departments and Staff:
  Manager - Chris Gay
Ages Represented: 14-22
Details: This agency works with young female models only.
Tips: Submit photos via email only. There are not open calls.

MC2 MODEL MANAGEMENT

6 W 14th Street, 2nd Floor, New York, NY 10011
Telephone: 646-638-3330 **Fax:** 646-638-2123
Website: www.mc2models.com **E-Mail:** myoffice@mc2mm.com
Ages Represented: 14+
Details: Represents models for runway and fashion print.
Tips: Submit by email or mail with subject line "New Faces." This agency has a minimum height requirement of 5'0".

MCDONALD/SELZNICK ASSOCIATES

1115 Broadway, Suite 1056, New York, NY 10010
Telephone: 646-237-6928 **Fax:** 646-253-1258
Website: www.msaagency.com
E-Mail: lucille@msaagency.com
Departments and Staff:
  Director- Lucille DicCampli
Ages Represented: Jul-60
Details: This agency specializes in dance, representing dancers, choreographers, as well as stage directors and production designers in the field of dance.
[SAG/AFTRA, AEA, ATA]

MEG PANTERA AGENCY

138 W 15th Street, 1st Floor, New York, NY 10011-6702
Telephone: 212-219-9330 **Fax:** 646-201-4119
Website: www.megpanteratheagency.com
E-Mail: theAgencySubmissions@gmail.com
Departments and Staff:
  Agent/Owner - Meg Pantera
  Sub Agent - Katie Murphy
Ages Represented: 18+
Details: This agency represents all types and ethnicities for theatre, film, and TV. They are known for working with strong character actors.

Tips: Meg will only consider mailed submissions. She does attend showcases and will consider all submissions personally.
[SAG/AFTRA, AEA]

METROPOLIS ARTISTS AGENCY

208 E 30th Street, Floor 2, New York, NY 10016-8202
Telephone: 212-779-0814 **Fax:** 212-545-1130
Website: www.metropolisagency.com
E-Mail: metropolisartists@gmail.com
Departments and Staff:
    President/Agent - Mariusz Bargielski,
    Agent - Patricia Roman
Details: This agency works with actors of all ages for commercials, film, TV, and theatre.
Tips: Submit headshots, resumes, and demos by mail or to newsubmissions@metropolisagency.com. Note that submission materials will not be returned. Interviews are by appointment only.
[SAG/AFTRA, AEA]

MINE, THE

420 Lexington Avenue, Suite 628, New York, NY 10170
Telephone: 212-612-3200 **E-Mail:** talent@the-mine.com
Departments and Staff:
    Owner/Agent - David Crombie;
    Agents - Dustin Flores, Paula Poeta
Details: They represents actors for TV, film, theatre, commercials, industrials, print, and soaps.
Tips: Submit through email or mail. Interviews are through appointment. No calls, faxes, or drop-ins.
[SAG/AFTRA, AEA, ATA, NATR]

MMG MODEL MANAGEMENT

1024 Sixth Avenue 2nd Floor, New York, NY 10018
Telephone: 212-253-8353 **Website:** www.nymmg.com
E-Mail: info@nymmg.com
Departments and Staff:
    President- Jeff Cohen
    Talent Manager- Aviva Skall
Details: MMG represents actors, hosts, and models in film, TV, commercials, voiceovers, music, appearances, and print.
Tips: They hold open calls for models on Wednesdays from 2-4 PM.

NOTES

MSA MODELS

200 West 41st Street, Suite 1000, New York, NY 10056
Telephone: 212-944-8896 **Fax:** 212-944-8899
Website: www.msamodels.com **E-Mail:** info@msamodels.com
Departments and Staff:
    President/CEO - Susan Levine;
    COO - William Ivers
Details: Represents models for commercials, print, runway, showroom, and fit models. They work with teens, adults, and seniors.
Tips: Complete the online representation request or attend an open call on Tuesday mornings. Applicants should provide at least one photo at the open call.

MSF TALENT

1350 Avenue of the Americas, 2nd Floor, New York, NY 10019
Telephone: 347-702-1488
E-Mail: submit@msftalentagency.com
Details: This agents hires for TV commercials, pilots, episodics and feature films, industrials, webisodes, voiceovers, and commercial print. They represent anyone from toddlers to seniors.
Tips: Send all submissions through mail or online. Under 18's should be submitted by a parent/guardian. No phone calls regarding submissions whatsoever.

N.S. BIENSTOCK, INC.

250 W 57th Street, Suite 333, New York, NY 10107
Telephone: 212-765-3040 **Fax:** 212-757-6411
Website: www.nsbienstock.com **E-Mail:** nsb@nsbtalent.com
Departments and Staff: President - Richard Leibner;
    Agents - Carole Cooper, Peter Godlberg, Myles Hazleton, George Hitzlik, Adam Leiber, Steve Sadicario, Stu Witt, Rick Ramage Lia Aponte, Jennifer Campanile,Paul Fedorko,Sid Kaufman,Ra Kumar,Samantha Marpe,JL Stermer;
    Host Programming - Steven DeVall
Details: Known as "The News Agency," N.S. Beinstock was established in 1964 and specializes in broadcast media but has also expanded to include: reality based programming/syndication, program development, co-production and distribution, radio, new media, entertainment executive representation, book publishing, and licensing and branding.
Tips: They accept submissions by mail and email (no personal drop-offs will not be accepted). If you are interested in becoming a client, please send a cover letter outlining your career goals

and a resume. For on-air talent also send a DVD of your work (maximum of 15 minutes in length). To submit to the literary department send a query letter via email, do not send attachments - if interested, you will receive a response in 4-6 weeks. Note: submission materials will not be returned.
[SAG/AFTRA]

NEW YORK MODEL MANAGEMENT

596 Broadway, Suite 701, New York, NY 10012
Telephone: 212-539-1700   **Fax:** 212-539-1775
Website: www.newyorkmodels.com
E-Mail: Women - scouting@newyorkmodels.com,
        Men - men@newyorkmodels.com
Departments and Staff:
    Marion Smith
Ages Represented: 6 months-12 years; Adult- 18+
Details: Represents children and young adults for fashion, print, and runway.
Tips: Submit photos by mail or email. Women can attend open calls every Thursday. If interested, the agency will be in touch for an interview.

NEXT MODELS

15 Watts Street, 6th Floor, New York, NY 10013,
Telephone: 212-925-5100   **Fax:** 212-925-5931
Website: www.nextmodels.com
E-Mail: submissions@nextmodels.com
Departments and Staff:
    Faith Kates, Joel Wilkenfeld, Leigh Crystal
Details: This agency works with models.
Tips: They accept submissions through mail and website.

NICOLOSI & CO.

150 W 25th Street, Suite 1200, New York, NY 10001-7404
Telephone: 212-633-1010   **Fax:** 212-633-0050
Website: www.nicolosi-co.com   **E-Mail:** info@nicolosi-co.com
Departments and Staff:
    Owner - Jeanne Nicolosi;
    Agents - David Cash, Jeremy Leiner; Assistant - Philip
    Carlson
Ages Represented: 18+
Details: A boutique talent agency representing actors for theatre, film, and TV.
Tips: Submit by mail.
[SAG/AFTRA AEA, NATR]

ONE MODEL MANAGEMENT

42 Bond Street, 2nd Floor, New York, NY 10012
Telephone: 212-505-5545 **Fax:** 212-431-1723
Website: www.onemanagement.com
E-Mail: one@onemanagement.com
Ages Represented: 14-20
Details: This agency works with models.
Tips: Submit by email or mail. They are looking for talent with the following height: 5'0" - 6'.

ORB MODEL MANAGEMENT

130 W 56th Street, Suite 4M, New York, NY 10019
Telephone: 212-957-2862 **Fax:** 212-957-3015
Website: www.orbmodels.com **E-Mail:** info@orbmodels.com
Departments and Staff:
   Tony Luffredo
Details: Works with models for runway, fashion print, and commercials.
Tips: Submit pictures/resumes through email. This agency hosts open calls on Thursday morning from 11am to noon.

PARADIGM

360 Park Avenue South, Floor 16, New York, NY 10010-1716
Telephone: 212-897-6400 **Fax:** 212-764-8941
Website: www.paradigmagency.com
Departments and Staff: Chairman - Sam Gores;
   Theatrical/Motion Pictures/TV - Sarah Fargo, Scott
   Metzger, Erin Castellanos, Richard Schmenner, Clifford
   Stevens, Timothy Sage, Fred Hashagen, John Domingos;
   Comedy/Personal Appearances - Matt Adair, Nate
   Herweyer, Kevin Kastrup, Seth Malasky;
   Voiceover - Jeb Bernstein, Olivia Catt, Matthew Smith, Matt
   Ambrosia, Joe O'Brien;
   Commercials (On-Camera) - Douglas Kesten, Stacye Mayer
Ages Represented: 18+
Details: This is a top ten agency. Paradigm represents actors, writers, musicians, and directors for film, TV, theatre, voiceovers, commercials, broadcast, and print.
Tips: Headshots and resumes can be sent via mail. No unsolicited demos accepted.
[DGA, SAG/AFTRA, AEA]

PARTS MODELS

PO Box 7529, FDR Station, New York, NY 10150
Telephone: 212-744-6123 **Fax:** 212-396-3014

Website: www.partsmodels.com
E-Mail: info@partsmodel.com
Details: This is a modeling agency that books work for specific body part modeling.
Tips: Submit pictures of a specific body part that is your specialty. Submit by email or mail.

PHOENIX ARTISTS, INC.

330 W 38th Street, Suite 607, New York, NY 10018
Telephone: 212-586-9110   **E-Mail:** phoenixartistsinc@gmail.com
Departments and Staff:
    Agents - Randi Ross, Gary Epstein;
    Assistant - Delores Williams
Details: They represent writers, directors, dancers, and actors of all ages for theatre, film, and TV.
Tips: Submissions should be sent by mail only. Interviews will be by appointment only.
[ATA, NATR, SAG/AFTRA, AEA]

PLAZA-7

1350 Avenue of the Americas, #386, New York, NY 10019
Telephone: 212-810-7501   **Website:** www.plaza7talent.com
E-Mail: plaza7talent@gmail.com
Departments and Staff:
    Agents - Francesca Grimaldi, Karen P. Parks, RJ;
    Murphy, Jodie Orellana, Kim Kleczka;
    TV Development - Sharon Parker; Assistant - Tracey
    Greenwich
Ages Represented: 6+
Details: Represent a wide range of performers including athletes, broadcasters, models, narrators and spokespersons for film, TV, commercials, industrials, music videos, commercial print, and voiceovers.
Tips: Submit headshots and resumes by mail only. Interviews will be granted by appointment only.
[SAG/AFTRA]

PRESTIGE MANAGEMENT GROUP

143 W 29th Street, Suite 1102, New York, NY 10001
Telephone: 212-239-6785   **Fax:** 212-239-6885
Website: www.prestigenyc.com   **E-Mail:** paula@prestigenyc.com
Departments and Staff:
    Founder - Paula Curcuru;
    Christopher D. Silveri; Children's Division - Tommy
    Prudenti

NOTES

Details: This agency will work with actors for commercials and print on a freelance basis, but it is largely a personal management agency that works with signed clients for film, TV, and theatre.

PRICE GROUP, LLC

33 W 19th Street 4th Floor New York, NY 10011
Telephone: 212-725-1980
Website: www.thepricegrouptalent.com
E-Mail: thepricegrouptalentagency@gmail.com
Departments and Staff:
    President/Agent - Lisa Price;
    Assistants - Jonathan Maserti, Alyceson Reyman
Ages Represented: 17+
Details: This agency works with adults for theatre, film, TV, and commercials.
Tips: Email your relevant links, headshots, and resume, or mail headshot and resume. Only accepting submissions from union talent.
[SAG/AFTRA, AEA]

PRODUCT MODEL MANAGEMENT

555 Eighth Avenue, Suite 710, New York, NY 10018
Telephone: 212-563-6444
Website: www.productmodelmgmt.com
E-Mail: info@take3talent.com
Departments and Staff: President - Natasha Matallana;
    Commercials/Commercial Print - Alyson Gaspin;
    Children's Division - Dariana Sub, Nathan Stolldorf
Details: Represents models for commercials and commercial print. They have an affiliation with Take 3 Talent that represents actors for film, TV, and theatre.
Tips: Submit by mail or online application. Interviews are by appointment only.
[SAG/AFTRA, AEA]

PROFESSIONAL ARTISTS

321 W 44th Street, Suite 605, New York, NY 10036-5457
Telephone: 212-247-8770
E-Mail: agents@professionalartists.net
Departments and Staff:
    Owners/Agents - Sheldon Lubliner, Marilynn Scott Murphy;
    Agent - Ashley Williams Landay
Ages Represented: 18+

Details: They represent adult actors and musical talent in theatre, film, and TV. This office also represents directors, choreographers, designers, and casting directors.
Tips: Submit by mail.
[SAG/AFTRA, AEA, WGA]

Q MODELS TALENT MANAGEMENT

354 Broadway, New York, NY 10013
Telephone: 212-807-6777 (Women); 212-807-6111 (Men)
Fax: 212-807-8999 **Website:** www.qmodels.com
E-Mail: nyc@qmanagementinc.com
Departments and Staff: Women - Jeffrey Kolsrud;
  Men - Natalie Kater
Details: A top modeling agency that works primarily with models for runway and fashion print. They will also work with actors for commercials, film, and TV.
Tips: Submit pictures and resumes through mail and through online form. There are also open call Wednesdays between 3:00 pm - 5:00 pm.
[SAG/AFTRA]

RED MODEL MANAGEMENT

302 W 37th Street, 3rd Floor, New York, NY 10018
Telephone: 212-785-1999 **Website:** www.rednyc.com
E-Mail: model@rednyc.com
Details: They represent models for runway, fashion print, and commercials.
Tips: Submit pictures/resumes through email.

RICK MILLER AGENCY, INC.

PO Box 2340, New York, NY 10021
Telephone: 212-242-8783 **Fax:** 212-242-8736
Website: www.rickmilleragencyinc.com
Departments and Staff: President/Agent - Rick Miller
Ages Represented: 20+
Details: This agency books for print, commercial, TV, and industrial.
Tips: This agency accepts headshots and resumes via mail only.
[AEA, SAG/AFTRA]

ROSS TALENT AGENCY

419 Lafayette Sreet, New York, NY 10003
Telephone: 646-684-4342

NOTES

E-Mail: submissions@rosstalentagency.com
Departments and Staff: Owner - Casey Ross
Ages Represented: 18+
Details: They represent all types (adult talent only) for commercials and commercial print.

ROSTER AGENCY, THE

247 W 38th Street, Floor 10, New York, NY 10018-4447
Telephone: 212-725-8459 **Website:** www.therosteragency.com
E-Mail: info@therosteragency.com
Departments and Staff:
   Owner/Agent - Michael W. Rodriguez
Details: All types of adults - no children - are represented in theatre, film, and TV.
Tips: They accept photos/resume by mail only and may attends showcases in an invitation is received. Materials will not be returned. They have a strict no phone calls nor walk-in/drop-off policy.
[SAG/AFTRA, AEA, NATR]

SILVER MODEL MANAGEMENT

630 Ninth Avenue, Suite 1401, New York, NY 10036-3741
Telephone: 212-966-1717 **Fax:** 212-966-1713
Website: www.silvermodels.com
E-Mail: info@silvermodels.com
Departments and Staff:
   President/Sports Fitness - Adam Silver;
   Film/TV/Commercial - Michael Lyons;
   Print/Film/TV/Commercial - Barry Godin;
   Sports Fitness - Adam Stango
Details: This agency represents talent for commercial print advertising, editorial, TV and feature films.
Tips: To submit materials to this agency, refer to the form on their website under the contacts tab and submit it via email. This agency hosts open casting calls, which take place every Thursday from 4PM to 5PM.

STANLEY KAPLAN TALENT

139 Fulton Street, New York, NY 10038
Telephone: 212-385-4400
E-Mail: info@stanleykaplantalent.com
Departments and Staff:
   Owner/Agent - Stanley Kaplan
Ages Represented: 2+
Details: This agency represents talent for commercials, TV, film, print, and music videos.

Tips: Subbmissions can be made through the website.
[SAG/AFTRA, AEA]

STEWART TALENT, NEW YORK

318 W 53rd Street, Room 201, New York, NY 10019-5742
Telephone: 212-315-5505 **Fax:** 646-448-0580
E-Mail: vony@stewarttalent.com
Website: www.stewarttalent.com/newyork
Departments and Staff:
    Owner - Jane Stewart;
    Co-Owner/NY President/Agent - Don Birge;
    Legit Dept - Tim Marshall, Kara Volkmann, Steve Maihack, Scott Tanzer;
    Promos/Voiceover - Marla Webergreen;
    Voiceover - Jason Sasportas;
    On-Camera Commercial - Phil Cassese;
    Jr. Agent/On-Camera - Amanda Nyman
Ages Represented: 18+
Details: This is a full service agency, whose talent includes, directors, voiceover artists, and actors for print, TV, film, commercial, and theatre.
Tips: Submit H/R to submissions.newyork.legit@stewarttalent. com for theatre/film/TV, or submissions.newyork.commercial@ stewarttalent.com for on-camera commercial; Submit an MP3 no longer than 3 minutes to vony@stewarttalent.com for voiceover.
[SAG/AFTRA, AEA]

STONE MANNERS SALNERS AGENCY

900 Broadway, Suite 910, New York, NY 10003-1249
Telephone: 212-505-1400 **Website:** www.smsagency.com
E-Mail: info@smsagency.com
Departments and Staff:
    Partner/Agent - Tim Stone;
    Agent - Ben Sands; Assistant - Samantha Huff
Details: This bi-coastal agency represents actors of all types, ages, and ethnicities in theatre, film, and TV.
Tips: Only submit by mail. Agents will accept postcards and invitations.
[SAG/AFTRA, AEA]

SW ARTISTS

888C 8th Avenue, #247, New York, NY 10019
Telephone: 646-246-8853 **Website:** www. sw-artists.com

NOTES

Departments and Staff:
Owner - Sue Winik
Details: This agency represents talent for theatre, film, TV, and commercials.
Tips: This agency accepts headshots, resumes, and demos by mail only.

TAKE 3 TALENT AGENCY

1460 Broadway, 8th Floor, New York, NY 10036
Telephone: 646-289-3915   **Website:** www.take3talent.com
E-Mail: info@take3talent.com
Departments and Staff:
Agents - Amanda Hall, Traci Jackson, Stephanie Clarke, Eddie Rabon, Natasha Matallana
Details: This agency handles all types and ages for theatre, film, TV, and print.
Tips: May submit via mail, email or online form. Include multiple photos and may include reels and demos. Typically only work with talent in the tri-state area. Visit their website for more detailed instructions on the Dos and Don'ts of their submissions.
[SAG/AFTRA, AEA]

TALENT HOUSE

325 W 38th Street, Room 605, New York, NY 10018-9642
Telephone: 212-957-5220   **Website:** www.talenthouse.ca
E-Mail: assistant@TTHNY.com
Departments and Staff: Agents - Peter Kaiser, Jed Abrahams
Details: This agency represents talent for film, TV, and theatre. They also have an office in Toronto.
Tips: This agency accepts headshots, resumes, and demos via mail only.
[NATR, SAG/AFTRA, AEA]

TALENT REPRESENTATIVES

307 E 44th St, Apt. F, New York, NY 10017
Telephone: 212-752-1835
Departments and Staff:
President - Honey Raider
Details: This agency represents actors for film and TV, as well as composers, models, TV writers, producers, and directors.
[DGA, WGA, NATR, SAG/AFTRA, AEA]

TALENT WORKS

505 8th Avenue, Suite 603, New York, NY 10018
Telephone: 212-889-0800   **Website:** www.talentworksny.com
E-Mail: mailroom@talentworksny.com
Departments and Staff:
    Partner - Harry Gold;
    Agents - Danielle Ippolito, Jay Kane
Details: This bi-coastal agency represents all ages for film, TV, and theatre.
Tips: Mail a hard copy picture and resume to their address. Be sure to include "ATTN: Talent Submission" in the address line. Drop-offs are not accepted.
[SAG/AFTRA, AEA, ATA]

THOMPSON MODEL AGENCY, INC.

330 W 65th Street, Suite 16E, New York, NY 10019
Telephone: 212-947-6711   **Fax:** 212-947-6732
Website: www.thompsonmodels.com
E-Mail: kimberlythompson@msn.com
Departments and Staff:
    Owner - Kim Thompson
Details: This agency books for commercials, print, high fashion, and runway.

UNITED TALENT AGENCY

888 Seventh Avenue, 9th Floor, New York, NY 10106
Telephone: 212-659-2600   **Website:** www.unitedtalent.com
Departments and Staff:
    Agents - Nancy Gates, Chris Highland, Mark Subias, Allison
    Wallach, Melissa Wells
Details: This is a top five agency. This agency books work for actors in the areas of film, TV, theatre, and voiceovers. They also represents screenwriters, playwrights, TV writers, directors, choreographers, and production designers. They are also located in Beverly Hills.
Tips: This agency accepts industry referrals only.
[AEA, SAG/AFTRA, DGA, WGA]

WILHELMINA CREATIVE MANAGEMENT

300 Park Avenue South, 2nd Floor, New York, NY 10010
Telephone: 212-473-0700, 212-473-1253 (Childrens Dept)
Fax: 212-473-3223   **Website:** www.wilhelmina.com

Departments and Staff:
Kids and Teens- David Gilbert, Teri Bostaji
Tips: This agency accepts submitted photos by email, offers open casting call, or hosts a Wilhelmina Model Search.

WILLIAM MORRIS ENDEAVOR ENT.

11 Madison Avenue, New York, NY 10010
Telephone: 212-586-5100 **Fax:** 212-246-3583
Website: www.wmeentertainment.com
Departments and Staff:
Partners - Dorian Karchmar Jon Rosen; Theatre - John Buzzetti; TV - Benjamin Simone; Music - Samantha Kirby
Details: This is a top five agency. They represent performance, creative, and technical talent in film, TV, music, publishing, and theatre. There are also locations in New York and London.
Tips: Industry referrals only. No submissions.
[SAG/AFTRA, AEA, NATR]

WOLF TALENT GROUP

165 W 46th Street, Suite 910, New York, NY 10036
Telephone: 212-840-6787 **E-Mail:** teresa@wolftalentgroup.com
Departments and Staff:
Owner/Theatrical/Equity - Teresa Wolf;
Theatrical/Equity - Frankie Moran ;
Assistant - Milly Millhauser
Ages Represented: 18+
Details: Wolf represents actors in theatre, film, TV, and commercials.
Tips: This agency prefers to be contacted by mail; they only accept hard copy submissions.
[SAG/AFTRA, AEA]

WOMEN MODEL MANAGEMENT/ SUPREME MANAGEMENT

199 Lafayette Street, 7th Floor, New York, NY 10012
Telephone:212-334-7480(Women) **Fax:** 212-334-7492
Website: www.womenmanagement.com
E-Mail:
info@womenmanagement.com;
info@suprememanagement.com
Ages Represented: 16-25
Details: Represents models for runway and fashion print.
Tips: They have a minumum height requirement of 5'9" for all talent interested in submitting.

ACTORS TALENT GROUP, INC.

410 South Michigan Avenue, Suite 733, Chicago, IL 60605
Telephone: 312-588-1309   **Fax:** 312-588-1579
Website: www.actorstalentgroup.com
E-Mail: talent-request@actorstalentgroup.com
Ages Represented: 18+
Details: This boutique agency represents for theatre, film, TV, commercials, print, news media, voiceovers and industrial.
Tips: New talent should provide a headshot and resume via mail or email. Questions should be handled through emails, not over the phone. Be advised: talent submission packages will not be returned. If accepted, you will hear from the agency within two weeks. Clients should be able to travel to the Chicago area for auditions on short notice.
[SAG/AFTRA, AEA, NON-UNION]

AMBASSADOR TALENT AGENTS

333 N Michigan Avenue suite 910, Chicago, IL 60601
Telephone: 312-641-3491
E-Mail: ambassadoragents@gmail.com
Departments and Staff: Director - Susan A. Sherman;
On-Camera Agent - Ed Cox
Ages Represented: 2 months+
Details: Ambassador Talent Agents, Inc. represents film, television, industrials, commercials, voice-over, print, runway and theater.
Tips: Interviews are conducted by appointment only. Headshots and resumes should be sent via mail only.
[SAG/AFTRA]

BIG MOUTH TALENT

900 N Franklin Street, Suite 403-1, Chicago, IL 60610-3124
Telephone: 312-421-4400   **Website:** www.bigmouthtalent.com
Departments and Staff: Owner - Brooke Tonneman, Kelly Wilkening
Details: Big Mouth Talent represents talent for film, TV, commercials, voiceovers, and print.
Tips: Interviews are granted by appointment only. Please send headshots and resumes by mail only "ATTN: New Talent"
[SAG/AFTRA, AEA]

NOTES

BMG TALENT GROUP

456 N May Street, Chicago, IL 60642-5819
Telephone: 312-829-9100 **Website:** www.bmgtalent.com
E-Mail: chicago@bmgtalent.com
Departments and Staff: President/CEO - Gregory S. Brown
Details: The Chicago talent division of BMG Models. They represent actors for film, TV and commercials.
Tips: Submit by mail.
[SAG/AFTRA]

DESANTI TALENTS, INC.

4241 W 63rd Street,1st Floor, Chicago, IL 60629
Telephone: 773-585-5843 **Fax:** 773-585-7201
Website: desantimodels.com
Departments and Staff:
   President/Agent - Susana DeSantiago;
Details: This agency represents all ages for print, broadcast, music, fashion, commercials, voiceovers, theatre, film, and TV. As a full service multi-cultural talent agency, DeSanti continues to be recognized as a leader in representing ethnic talent nationally.
Tips: Photos, resumes, and demos should be mailed or emailed depending on which department you choose to submit to. Union and non-union adult talent should mail materials, kids and voiceover artists should email Mfavela@desantimodels.com or Dtalents@aol.com, respectively.
[SAG/AFTRA]

EMMRICH AGENCY

5103 Turnberry Court, Plainfield, IL 60586
Telephone: 815-577-8650 **Fax:** 773-585-7201

GRAY TALENT GROUP

727 S Dearborn Street, Suite 312, Chicago, IL 60605
Telephone: 312-663-1659 **Fax:** 312-663-1797
Website: www.graytalentgroup.com
E-Mail: graytalentgroup@gmail.com
Departments and Staff:
   President - Dawn Gray;
   Associate Agents - Maggie McCoy, Chris Gonyo
   Agent - Kiki Kapral
Ages Represented: 5+
Details: They book talent for film, theatre, commercials, voiceovers, industrials, website and print advertisements.

Tips: Send headshot and resume (attached), self-addressed stamped envelope, and a demo Reel (if available) by mail only. **[SAG/AFTRA, AEA]**

GROSSMAN & JACK TALENT, INC.

33 W Grand Avenue, Suite 402, Chicago, IL 60654
Telephone: 312-587-1155 **Fax:** 312-587-2122
Website: www.grossmanjack.com
E-Mail: info@grossmanjack.com
Departments and Staff:
Owner/Voiceover Agent - Linda Jack;
On Camera/Theatrical -Bob Schroeder, Jess Jones,Donna Simon Dunn
Voiceover - Susan Farlik, Vanessa Lanier
Details: They book talent of all ages for print, commercials, voiceovers, film, TV, and theatre.
Tips: Submit headshot, resume, and demos by mail or email. Interviews will be conducted by appointment only.
[SAG/AFTRA, AEA]

KIMBERLY KATZ TALENT

4422 N Ravenswood, Chicago, IL 60640
Telephone: 708-259-1970
Website: www.kimberlykatztalent.com
E-Mail: submissions@kimberlykatztalent.com
Departments and Staff:
Agents - Kimberly Katz, Ken Payne, Jason Royal
Details: They represent talent for film, TV, and theatre.
Tips: New submissions can be sent via email.
[SAG/AFTRA]

LILY'S TALENT

1017 W Washington Boulevard, Suite 4F, Chicago, IL 60607-2110
Telephone: 312-601-2345 **Fax:** 312-601-2353
Website: www.lilystalent.com **E-Mail:** info@lilystalent.com
Departments and Staff:
President/Agent - Lily Liu;
Vice President Andrea Shipp
Agency Director - Oliver Al;
Commercial/Theatrical - Stephanie Potakis;
Voiceover - Calle Hack; Music - AC Mangabut;
Print - Sarah Sapien

NOTES

Details: They work with all ages for print, commercials, voiceovers, film, TV, and theatre.

Tips: Submissions are accepted by mail and through the online submission form. Interviews are granted by appointment only.

[SAG/AFTRA, AFM, WGA]

NAKED VOICES, INC.

900 N Franklin Street, Suite 709, Chicago, IL 60610-3124
Telephone: 312-563-0136 **Website:** www.nakedvoices.com
E-Mail: info@nakedvoices.com
Departments and Staff:
   Agents - Deb Kotzen, Brett Sechrist, Laurie Haverkamp
Ages Represented: 8+
Details: This agency represents voiceover artists of all ages.
Tips: Submit one copy of your demo via mail. The agency does not accept email, walk-in, or drop-off submissions. Demo CDs should be no longer than one minute. Interviews are granted by appointment only.

[SAG/AFTRA]

PAONESSA TALENT AGENCY

1512 N Fremont Street, Suite 105, Chicago, IL 60642
Telephone: 773-360-8749 **Fax:** 773-360-8764
Website: www.paonessatalent.com
E-Mail: paonessatalentagency@yahoo.com
Departments and Staff:
   President/Agent - Marisa Paonessa;
   Talent Agent - Samantha Siroky
   Talent Associate- Nicole Zender
Details: Represents actors for film, TV, theatre, commercials, and voiceovers.
Tips: Submissions accepted by mail only. Include a SASE. Interviews are by appointment only.

[SAG/AFTRA, NON-UNION]

POLTUN ENTERTAINMENT GROUP

PO Box 805644, Chicago, IL 60680
Telephone: 312-953-1054
Website: www.onthelist.poltunentertainment.com
E-Mail: steve@poltunentertainment.com

SHIRLEY HAMILTON

333 E Ontario Street, Chicago, IL 60611-4804
Telephone: 312-787-4700

Website: www.shirleyhamiltontalent.com
E-Mail: Lynne@shirleyhamilton.com
Departments and Staff: Agency Director - Lynne Hamilton;
   Print Agent - Laurie Hamilton;
   Theatre/Commercial- Renee Keen
   Film/Commericla- KaCee Hudson
Ages Represented: All ages.
Details: This agency represents talent for film, TV, theatre, voiceovers, as well as print.
Tips: Submit through mail. No submissions by email.
[SAG/AFTRA, AEA]

STEWART TALENT

58 W Huron Street, Chicago, IL 60654-3806
Telephone: 312-943-3131   **Fax:** 312-943-0527
Website: stewarttalent.com
Departments and Staff: President - Jane Stewart;
   Industrial/TV/Film, Adults - Casey Janney
   Commercial Print - Wade Childress;
   Voiceover - Sheila Dougherty, Joan Sparks;
   Print, Kids - Kathi Gardner;
   TV/Film/Theatre, Adults - Sam Samuelson;
   Commercial Print, Adults/Kids - Jenn Hall;
   TV/Film, Adults/Kids - Jenny Wilson, Todd Turina
   Voiceover- Kim Valkenburg
Details: This is a full service agency, whose talent includes models, sports personalities, directors, voiceover artists, and actors for print, TV, film, commercial, and theatre.
Tips: This agency accepts headshots and resumes via email to chicago.legit@stewarttalent.com; For voiceover submissions, send an MP3 no longer than 3 min. to vo@stewarttalent.com; See website for addition submission requirements.
[SAG/AFTRA, AEA]

ACTION FIGURES INTERNATIONAL

2990 Grace Lane, Costa Mesa, CA 92626-4120
Telephone: 714-545*1473   **Fax:** 714-545-3437
Website: www.actionfiguresinternational.com
E-Mail: info@actionfiguresinternational.com
Details: This agency represents "action talent" for film, TV, print and stage. They cover all levels of stunt work, including fight choreography and weapon work. Additionally represents graffiti artists.
Tips: Interested applicants can contact this agency through their website.

ACTORS GROUP

9703 SW 264th Street, Vashon, WA 98070
Telephone: 206-427-7449   **Fax:** 206-463-0779
Website: www.theactorsgroup.com
E-Mail: info@theactorsgroup.com
Departments and Staff:
  Owner/Agent - Jamie Lopez
Ages Represented: 20+
Details: This agency represents actors for film, TV, commercials, and voiceover. They also represent writers, directors, print models, comedians, broadcast journalists, newscasters, and hosts & MCs.
Tips: Submissions may be send by mail or email, however email is preferred. Interviews are made by appointment only.
[SAG/AFTRA, AEA]

AGENCY CONNECTS LLC

605 Corporate Drive West, Langhorne, PA 19047
Telephone: 267-577-0590   **Website:** www.agencyconnects.com
E-Mail: AgencyConnects@gmail.com
Ages Represented: 6+
Details: Agency Connects, LLC represents talent of all ages for film, TV, voiceovers, commercials, print, industrials, and theatre.
Tips: Submissions, consisting of a headshot and resume, will only be accepted via mail. Child submissions will be accepted by recommendation only.
[SAG/AFTRA, AEA, NON-UNION]

AMA TALENT AGENCY

93 Old York Road, Suite 1 #515, Jenkintown, PA 19046
Telephone: 215-885-7711   **Website:** www.amatalentagency.com

E-Mail: info@amatalentagency.com
Departments and Staff:
Agents - Mary Lennon, Roe Lennon
Details: Books talent for film, TV, theatre, commercials, voiceovers, industrials, and commercial print.
Tips: Headshots and resumes can be sent by mail or via the agency's online registration form.
[SAG/AFTRA, NON-UNION]

AVENUE ACTORS AGENCY

1209 4th Ave North, Suite B, Nashville, TN 37208
Telephone: 615-293-9648
Website: www.theavenueagency.com
Details: Represents men, women, and children, booking for high fashion, movies, print, promotion, TV episodes/series, commercial, and voiceover work.
[SAG/AFTRA]

AXIS MODELS & TALENT, INC.

PO Box 367, Ringwood, NJ 07456
Telephone: 973-248-8040 **Fax:** 973-248-8042
Website: www.axismodelsandtalent.com
E-Mail: axismodelstalent@yahoo.com
Departments and Staff:
Executive/Talent Agent - Dwight Brown
Details: This agency works primarily in the NY area. They represent talent for commercials and commercial print.
Tips: The agency requires both a full length photo and a headshot in the submission package. Additional information regarding submissions can be found on the agency's website. No unsolicited calls.

BOCA TALENT & MODEL

2640 Hollywood Boulevard, Suite 100, Hollywood, FL 33020
Telephone: 954-428-4677 **Fax:** 954-429-9203
Website: www.bocamodels.com **E-Mail:** info@bocamodels.com
Departments and Staff:
Owner - Natalie Toewe
Manager - Laura Forster;
Talent Agents - Elissa Dimig, Regina Walker
Ages Represented: 3+
Details: Boca Talent and Model Agency represents talent of all ages in a variety of disciplines, including print, broadcast, voiceovers, film, and TV.

NOTES

Tips: Applicants should submit an online profile, which can be found at the agency's website. Interviews will be held by appointment only.
[SAG/AFTRA, AEA]

BOOM MODELS & TALENT

2339 3rd Street, #49, San Francisco, CA 94107
Telephone: 415-626-6591 **Website:** www.boomagency.com
E-Mail: boomagency@sbcglobal.net
Departments and Staff:
 Owners/Agents - Kristen Usich, John E. Hutcheson
Ages Represented: All ages.
Details: This agency represents talent for TV, commercials, film, animation, runway, commercial and fashion print, catalog, and voiceovers.
Tips: In order to apply for representation send photos, headshots, zed cards, or snapshots with a resume (if applicable) and cover letter. You can send an email or regular mail marked: "ATTN: New Faces."
[SAG/AFTRA]

BOWMAN AGENCY, THE

PO Box 4071, Lancaster, PA 17604
Telephone: 717-898-7716 **Fax:** 717-898-6084
Website: www.thebowmanagency.com
E-Mail: mlbowman@thebowmanagency.com
Departments and Staff:
 Owner/Director - Mary Bowman
Details: They work with actors and models. They book for film, TV, commercials, runway, and print.
Tips: Headshots and resumes can be submitted by mail or email. Interviews are held by appointment only.

BRAND MODEL & TALENT

601 N Baker Street, Santa Ana, CA 92703
Telephone: 714-850-1158
Website: www.brandtalent.com
E-Mail: info@brandtalent.net
Details: Brand represents both models and talent with divisions in Fashion Print, Plus Size, Runway, Kids, Lifestyle Commercial Print, Promotions, Showroom, Fit, and Television Commercials.
[SAG/AFTRA]

BREVARD TALENT

100 S Eola Drive, Suite 200, Orlando, FL 32801
Telephone: 407-841-7775 **Fax:** 407-841-7716
Website: www.brevardtalentgroup.com
E-Mail: Traci@BrevardTalentGroup.com
Departments and Staff:
    President - Traci Danielle
Ages Represented: 5+
Details: This agency works with talent of all ages for commercials, voiceovers, film, and TV.
Tips: Submissions should be sent via mail. No walk-ins allowed. For voiceovers, send a CD and resume by mail. If the CD should be returned, please include a self-addressed stamped envelope.
[SAG/AFTRA, AEA]

CAPITAL TALENT AGENCY, LLC

1330 Connecticut Avenue NW, Suite 271, Washington, DC 20036
Telephone: 202-429-4785
Website: www.capitaltalentagency.com
E-Mail: roger@capitaltalentagency.com
Departments and Staff:
    CEO/Agent - Roger Yoerges
    Agents - J. Fred Shiffman, Rich Luna, Rachel Swan
Ages Represented: 18+
Details: They works with actors, directors, choreographers, and writers for print, film, TV, theatre, commercials, and voiceovers.
Tips: Submit hard copies of headshots, resumes, reels, and/or clips by mail "ATTN: Submissions." No phone calls please.
[SAG/AFTRA, AEA]

CINDY ROMANO
MODEL & TALENT AGENCY

P.O. Box 1951, Palm Springs, CA 92263
Telephone: 760-323-3333 **Website:** cindyromanotalent.com
Details: This agency represents actors for commercial work and modeling.
Tips: Submit by mail.

CLICK MODELS

216 Green Tree Drive, Westchester, PA 19382
Telephone: 610-399-0700 **Fax:** 610-399-3004

NOTES

Website: www.clickmodel.com **E-Mail:** clickmodelspa@aol.com
Departments and Staff:
  Renee Lauren
Details: This agency represents models for runway, fashion print, and commercials.
Tips: Headshots and resumes can be submitted by mail or email. Submission forms can be filled out through their website. Interviews are held by appointment only.

COCONUT GROVE TALENT

3525 Vista Court, Miami, FL 33133
Telephone: 305-858-3002 **Website:** coconutgrovetalent.com
E-Mail: contact@coconutgrovetalent.com
Departments and Staff:
  Owner/Agent - Cathy Tully;
  Assistant - Angela Toffoli
Details: This agency represents all ages for print, commercials, voiceovers, film, and TV.
Tips: Submissions can be sent via mail only. Interviews will be granted by appointment only.
[SAG/AFTRA, AEA, WGA]

DOCHERTY AGENCY, THE

109 Market Street, Pittsburgh, PA 15222
Telephone: 412-765-1400 **Fax:** 412-765-0403
Website: www.dochertyagency.com
E-Mail: pittsburgh@dochertyagency.com
Departments and Staff:
  Owner/Agent - Deb Docherty
Details: This agency also has offices in Cleveland, OH. They represents babies through seniors for film, TV, commercials, and voiceovers.
Tips: Sumissions are accepted via mail or the application found on the website. Interviews granted by appointment only. There are also open calls the first Tuesday of every month between 3:30 and 4:40 pm. Bring headshots and resumes.
[SAG/AFTRA]

DONATELLI MODELS AGENCY

156 Madison Avenue,Reading, PA 19605
Telephone: 610-921-0777 **Website:** www.donatellimodels.com
E-Mail: Randy@donatellimodels.com
Departments and Staff:
  President - Tony L. Donatelli;
  Mickey Donatelli, Randy Donatelli

Ages Represented: 18+
Details: This agency works with adult models and actors in the areas of film, TV, commercials, print, and trade shows.
Tips: Complete the online application and call to set up an appointment. A $10 refundable fee will be charged prior to the interview time.

ELEGANCE TALENT AGENCY

2763 State Street, Carlsbad, CA 92008
Telephone: 760-434-3397 **Website:** www.eletalent.com
E-Mail: eletalent@sbcglobal.net
Departments and Staff:
    Owner/Agent - Pam Pahnke
Ages Represented: 2+
Details: This agency has been booking actors for TV, films, commercials, video, voiceovers, print, runway, promotions, and trade shows since 1991. They work with children and adults.
Tips: They accept resumes by email, but other materials are only accepted by mail. They ask that you include a self addressed stamped envelope with any submissions.
[SAG/AFTRA]

EMERGING TALENT LLC

840 N Wood Avenue, Linden, NJ 07036-4038
Telephone: 732-207-7696 **Website:** www.emergingtalentllc.com
Details: They book young models and actors for print, commercials, voiceovers, film, and TV.
Tips: Headshots and resumes can be sent by mail. Submissions should be sent to NY office- 132 West 31st StreetSte. 1505 New York, NY 10001 Postcards and invitations are also accepted. Interviews will be conducted by appointment only.
[SAG/AFTRA, AEA]

EXPRESSIONS MODEL & TALENT

860 First Avenue - Suite 7B King of Prussia, PA 19406
Telephone: 484-318-8776
Website: www.expressionsmodels.com
E-Mail: info@expressionsmodels.com
Departments and Staff:
    Owner/Agent - Dianna Juliano;
    Agent - Greer Lange
Ages Represented: 5+
Details: All ethnicities and ages are represent in modelling, acting, and dance. They focus in the areas of TV, film, all areas of modeling, commercials, print industrials, and promos.

NOTES

Tips: Do not drop-in unless you have an appointment. Submission by mail and website (through the Talent Application).
[SAG/AFTRA, AEA]

FRESH FACES AGENCY, INC.

2911 Carnation Avenue, Baldwin, NY 11510-4402
Telephone: 516-223-0034 **Website:** www.freshfacesagency.com
E-Mail: talent@freshfacesagency.com
Departments and Staff: President - Aggie Gold
Details: This agency specializes in representing children.
Tips: For representation, send a headshot (snapshots are ok for kids under 5) and a resume. Include a self-addressed stamped envelope if you would like materials returned. If headhots and resume are sent through e-mail, include them in the body, not as an attachment.
[SAG/AFTRA, AEA]

GREER LANGE & ASSOCIATES

3 Bala Plaza West, Suite 201, Bala Cynwyd, PA 19004
Telephone: 610-747-0300 **Fax:** 610-747-0330
Website: www.greerlange.com **E-Mail:** info@GreerLange.com
Departments and Staff: Senior Booking Agent - Daniel Agosta
Details: This agency represents talent for commercials, voiceover, print, runway, film, and TV.
Tips: Submissions are accepted by mail and through the online submission form. Interviews are granted by appointment only.
[SAG/AFTRA, AEA]

HAMPTON MODELS

811 W Jericho Turnpike, Suite 107E, Smithtown, NY 11787
Telephone: 631-366-0200 **Fax:** 631-366-0236
Website: www.thehamptonmodels.com
E-Mail: submit@thehamptonmodels.com
Departments and Staff: President - Allie Cresswell
Details: They represent all ages for film, TV, commercials, fashion, and print.
Tips: Submit a headshot, resume, and reel via email. Interviews are granted by appointment only.
[SAG/AFTRA, NON-UNION]

HEYMAN TALENT

772 N. Highway Street, Suite 207, Columbus, OH 43215
Telephone: 614-291-8200 **Fax:** 614-291-8201
Website: www.heymantalent.com

E-Mail: infocolumbus@heymantalent.com
Departments and Staff:
    Director/Agent - Michael Owen
Ages Represented: 5+
Details: Heyman Talent has several offices throughout the country and they work with actors, voiceover artists, models, stylists, and makeup artists. They also often represent hosts, variety artists, and animation artists.
Tips: Applicants can complete an online submission form or mail a headshot and resume. Interviews are held by appointment only.
[SAG/AFTRA]

IKON MODEL MANAGEMENT

PO Box 612, Oldwick, NJ 08858
Telephone: 212-691-2363 **Website:** www.ikonmodels.com
E-Mail: info@ikonmodels.com
Departments and Staff: Cynthia Saldan
Details: This agencey works with models.
Tips: Submissions may be emailed in.

JE TALENT

323 Geary Street, Suite 302, San Francisco, CA 94102
Telephone: 415-395-9475 **Fax:** 415-395-9301
E-Mail: info@jetalent.com
Departments and Staff: Owner/Agent - John Erlendson;
    Director/Models - Phillip Gums;
    Theatrical/Commercial - Kate Hansen, Dee Dee
    Shaughnessey;
    Voiceover - Seth Podowitz;
    Youth - Nikki Duarte, Shannon Escoto
Details: This successful San Francisco agency is proud to represent award winning talent for film, TV, commercial, corporate, and voiceover work. They also represent hair and makeup stylists.
Tips: Submisions are accepted by mail or by email.
[SAG/AFTRA, AEA]

JO ANDERSON MODEL & TALENT LLC

1 Eves Drive, Suite 111, Marlton, NJ 08053
Telephone: 856-596-7200
Website: www.joandersonmodels.com
E-Mail: JATalent1@gmail.com
Departments and Staff:
    Owner - Kathi Anderson
Details: Represents models and actors for film, TV, commercials and commercial print.

NOTES

JOHNSTON AGENCY

45 Grove Street, New Canaan, CT 06840
Telephone: 203-838-6188   **Fax:** 203-838-6642
Departments and Staff:
  Commercial Print - Toni Curcio;
  Commercials/Voiceovers - Debbie Chasen;
  Commercial Print/Childrens Division - Dawn Woods-King
Details: They represents actors and models of all ages for commercials, voiceovers, print, fashion, film, and TV.
Tips: Applicants can complete an online submission form or mail a headshot and resume. Interviews are held by appointment only.

KIDS INTERNATIONAL

938 E Swan Creek Road, Box 152, Fort Washington, MD 20744
Telephone: 301-292-6094   **Fax:** 301-292-7965
Website: www.kidsinternationaltalentagency.com
E-Mail: kitalent99@verizon.net
Departments and Staff:
  Owners/Agents - Samuel and Barbara Love
Ages Represented: 3+
Details: This agency represents all ages for print, commercials, voiceovers, theatre, film, and TV.
Tips: Send headshots and resumes by mail. Interviews will be held by appointment only.
[SAG/AFTRA, AEA]

LEVEL TALENT GROUP

3214 W Kennedy Blvd Tampa, FL 33609
Telephone: 813-814-4944   **Fax:** 813-814-4456
Website: www.leveltalentgroup.com
E-Mail: info@leveltalentgroup.com
Departments and Staff:
  President - Kelly Paige;
  Director - Darcy Britton
Details: They represent talent for fashion, print, film, and TV.
Tips: Interested parties can apply by email to submissions@ leveltalentgroup.com or the completion of the agency's online submission form. Interviews will be conducted by appointment only.
SAG/AFTRA

LOOK TALENT

166 Geary Street, Suite 1406, San Francisco, CA 94108
Telephone: 415-781-2841 **Fax:** 415-781-5722
Website: www.looktalent.com **E-Mail:** joan@looktalent.com
Departments and Staff:
Director of Talent/Agent - Joan Spangler
Ages Represented: 18+
Details: Look represents actors in national and regional commercials, as well as print advertisements, film, and live corporate events.
Tips: Submissions are only accepted by mail and must include a cover letter (letter of introduction), a current 8 X 10" headshot or composite, resume , your CD if you are interested in doing voice-over work in a self-addressed stamped envelope(if you want a guaranteed reply). Please mark ATTN: Joan Spangler.
[SAG/AFTRA, AEA]

LYNNE C. & COMPANY

PO Box 284, Bellmore, NY 11710
Telephone: 516-765-3616
Website: www.modelsandeventstaff.com
E-Mail: info@lynnecandcompany.com
Departments and Staff:
Owner - Lynne Carole
Details: Represents young adults through seniors for commercials, commercial print, industrials, events, and trade shows.
Tips: This agency works primarily with non-union talent. They are currently seeking models and tradeshow spokespersons. Submissions are accepted through online application.

MARLA DELL
TALENT AGENCY, INC.

2124 Union Street, #C, San Francisco, CA 94123
Telephone: 415-563-9213 **Fax:** 415-563-9213
Website: mdtagencysf.com
E-Mail: reception@mtdagencysf.com
Departments and Staff:
President/Models - Michelle Mokalla;
On-Camera/Voiceover - Nicole Younce;
Print/Tradeshow Agent - Olivia Tehrani
Details: This agency represents talent of all ages for commercials, print, voiceovers, film, and conventions.

NOTES

Tips: Submissions are accepted by mail or online and differ by department.
[SAG/AFTRA]

MARY ANNE CLARO

8600 West Chester Pike, Suite 202, Upper Darby, PA 19082
Telephone: 484 452 6434 **Fax:** 484-452-6437
Website: www.clarotalent.net **E-Mail:** rocco1513@aol.com
Departments and Staff:
   Owner/Agent - Mary Anne Claro; Children - Ray Claro
Details: This agency represents all ages in the areas of film, TV, theatre, voiceover. They also represent many foreign language performers.
Tips: Send headshot (recent professional photo may be accepted in lieu of a headshot) and resume through mail, making sure to include a contact number. Represents talent outside of NYC; will work with both union and non-union actors.
[SAG/AFTRA, AEA]

MMA/MODEL MANAGEMENT AGENCY

106 South Bellevue Avenue, Suite 212, Langhorne, PA 19047
Telephone: 215-752-8603 **Fax:** 215-752-8604
Website: www.mmaagency.com **E-Mail:** info@mmaagency.com
Departments and Staff:
   Founder/Director - Ellen Wasser-Hrin;
   Assistant Director - Sarah G. Howell;
   Children - Lindsey Catherine
Details: They represent actors and models for film, TV, commercials, voiceovers, hosting, runway, and fashion print
Tips: Submit photos by mail only. If the agency is interested, applicants will be invited to attend an open call.

MOORE CREATIVE TALENT

3130 Excelsior Boulevard, Minneapolis, MN 55416
Telephone: 612-827-3200 **Website:** www.mooretalent.com
E-Mail: oncamera@mooretalent.com
Departments and Staff:
   President - Andrea Hjelm;
   Agents - Carol McCormick
Details: This agency represents models and actors of all ages for print, fashion, voiceovers, commercials, film, and TV.

Tips: They do not hold open calls or accept email correspondence. Please submit headshots and resumes by mail only. Interviews will be granted by appointment only.
[SAG/AFTRA, AEA]

OTTO MODELS CORP.

2901 West Coast Highway, #350, Newport Beach, CA 92663
Telephone: 949-258-4329 **Website:** www.ottomodels.com
E-Mail: jason@ottomodels.com
Departments and Staff:
    Founders - Jason Ozzo, Tereza Otto, Sal Reyes
Details: This agency represents talent in print, commercials, and modeling.
Tips: This agency does not have open calls, it is by appointment ONLY. If you are interested in being represented, please submit your photos; whichever you feel best represents yourself. Submit to newfaces@ottomodels.com

PEAK MODELS & TALENT

280 N. Westlake Boulevard, #110, Westlake Village, CA 91362
Telephone: 818-889-8800 **Website:** www.peakmodels.com
E-Mail: info@peakmodels.com
Departments and Staff:
    Co-Owner/CEO - Natasha Duswalt;
    Co-Owner - Craig Duswalt;
    Senior Booker - Taylor Borland
Details: This agency represents talent for print, modeling, voiceover, commercials, film, TV, and dance.
Tips: Submissions are accepted by email only. Interviews are by appointment.
[SAG/AFTRA]

REINHARD, INC.

2021 Arch Street, Suite 400, Philadelphia, PA 19103
Telephone: 215-567-2000 **Website:** www.reinhardagency.com
E-Mail: info@reinhardagency.com
Departments and Staff:
    Owner - Virginia B. Doyle;
    Agent - M.G. Eisenhart, Jenna Adams; Lauren Giarrocco
    Agency Director/Print Division: Jenna Adams,
    Runway Division: Lauren Giarrocco,
    Talent Division: Olivia Hoff
Ages Represented: 3+
Details: This agency represents talent for film, TV, and commercials, and also models for print and runway.

NOTES

Tips: This agency accepts headshots and resumes via mail. Submissions can be sent to Submissions: submissions@reinhardagency.com,

SAN DIEGO MODEL MANAGEMENT

438 Camino Del Rio Street, #116, San Diego, CA 92108
Telephone: 619-296-1018   **Website:** www.sdmodel.com
E-Mail: info@sdmodel.com
Departments and Staff:
    President - Fred Sweet;
    Agency Director - Linda Comer;
    Kids/Promo -Jennifer Fite
Details: Represents print models, runway models, infants and actors commercials, film, and TV.
Tips: Submissions accepted by mail or email.
[SAG/AFTRA]

SANGER TALENT AGENCY

121 N Harbor Boulevard, #A, Fullerton, CA 92832
Telephone: 800-828-8582   **Website:** www.sangertalent.com
E-Mail: karl@sangertalent.com
Departments and Staff:
    Owner/Agent - Karl B. Sanger
Details: Represents composers, comedians, broadcast journalists and newscasters, TV writers, music artists, host and MCs, magicians, screenwriters, animation artists, music editors, sports personalities, dancers, musical theatre performers as well as actors in TV, film and commercials.
Tips: Submissions accepted by mail or email.   Interviews by appointment only.

SHAMON FREITAS
TALENT AGENCY

3916 Oregon Street, San Diego, CA 92104
Telephone: 619-325-1180   **Fax:** 619-325-1183
Website: www.shamonfreitas.com
E-Mail: general@shamonfreitas.com
Departments and Staff:
    Owner/Agent - Carol S. Freitas;
    Agents - Dana Berardinelli, Frank DiPalermo
Ages Represented: 5+
Details: They handle models and actors of all ages for print, commercials, film, TV, and voiceovers.

Tips: Send submissions by mail or email to submissions@ shamonfreitas.com. The agency does not accept walk-ins or have open calls. Interviews will be given by appointment only.
[SAG/AFTRA, AEA]

STARS: THE AGENCY

23 Grant Avenue, Floor 4, San Francisco, CA 94108
Telephone: 415-421-6272   **Fax:** 415-421-7620
Website: www.starsagency.com   **E-Mail:** info@starsagency.com
Departments and Staff:
  CEO - Lynn Claxon;
  President/Talent Division - Kristin Claxon Stinnett;
  President/Model Management - Scott Claxon;
  Talent - Nate Tico, Alessandra Rohde; Voiceover - Brian
  Burge;
  Children - Elena Ng; Print/Runway - Alicia Mason, Amy
  Jones;
  New Faces - Kristen Kotik
Details: This agency represents talent of all ages for print, fashion, commercials, voiceovers, industrials, theatre, film, and TV.
Tips: Interested parties can upload submission materials to the website. Interviews will be conducted by appointment only.
[SAG/AFTRA, AEA, ATA, WGA, DGA]

TALENT PLUS/
LATINOS AGENCY

318 Rhine Ct, Salinas, CA 93906
Telephone: 831-443-5542   **Fax:** 831-443-5542
Website: www.talentplusloslatinos.com
Departments and Staff:
  Director - Gail Jones;
  Co-Director - Richmond Brock
Ages Represented: 5+
Details: This agency represents talent for print, broadcast, voiceovers, commercials, film, and TV. They specialize in Hispanic talent.
Tips: Submit a headshot, cover letter, resume, and demo by mail only to Gail Jones, 318 Rhine Court, Salinas, CA 93906. Interviews are granted by appointment only.
[SAG/AFTRA]

TONRY TALENT

885 Bryant Street, #201, San Francisco, CA 94103
Telephone: 415-543-3797   **Fax:** 415-957-9656
Website: www.tonrytalent.com

E-Mail: tonry@tonrytalent.com
Departments and Staff:
   Owner/Agent - Mary Tonry
Ages Represented: 18+
Details: Tonry Talent works with adult actors of all types, particularly in voiceover work.
Tips: Submit headshot,resume, letter of interest, Demo CD (for voiceover) in a self-addressed, stamped envelope by mail only.
[SAG/AFTRA, NON-UNION, AEA]

WEHMANN MODELS TALENT, INC.

1128 Harmon Place, Suite 202, Minneapolis, MN 55403
Telephone: 612-333-6393   **Website:** www.wehmann.com
E-Mail: swehmann@wehmann.com
Departments and Staff:
   President - Susan Wehmann;
   On-Camera - Lucia Stuessi; Voiceover - Amy Oppegaard;
   Print/Runway - Megan Tadewald; Print - Julia Wolfe
Details: This agency represents actors for commercials, film, and TV, as well as print models, hosts & MCs, runway models, and voiceover artists. They work with all ages.
Tips: This agency accepts headshots and resume by an online form or mail.
[SAG/AFTRA]

YOUTH TALENT CONNECTION

17332 Irvine Boulevard, #230, Tustin, CA 92780
Telephone: 714-315-8546   **Fax:** 714-505-3062
Website: www.youthtalentconnection.com
E-Mail: youthtalentinfo@yahoo.com
Departments and Staff:
   Heather Baldwin
Details: This agency books talent of all ages for film, TV, theatre, commercials, print, and industrials.
Tips: Submissions can be sent via mail or email at ytcnewclient@yahoo.com with the subject heading "New Client."
[SAG/AFTRA]